A
Harlequin
Romance

OTHER
Harlequin Romances
by ANNE HAMPSON

Many of these titles are available at your local bookseller,
or through the Harlequin Reader Service.

For a free catalogue listing all available Harlequin Romances,
send your name and address to:

HARLEQUIN READER SERVICE,
M.P.O. Box 707, Niagara Falls, N.Y. 14302
Canadian address: Stratford, Ontario, Canada.

or use order coupon at back of book.

THERE CAME
A TYRANT

by

ANNE HAMPSON

HARLEQUIN BOOKS   TORONTO
WINNIPEG

Original hard cover edition published in 1972
by Mills & Boon Limited, 17-19 Foley Street,
London   W1A 1DR, England

© Anne Hampson 1972

Harlequin edition published September, 1972

SBN 373-01622-0

Printed in Canada

CHAPTER ONE

THE crew of the VC 10 were gathered in the squadron room at R.A.F. Sedenlowe, where the pilot, Squadron Leader Travers, was finalizing the plans for tomorrow's flight to Bahrain.

All the men had spoken – the co-pilot, Flight Lieutenant Miles Schofield, the navigator, Flight Lieutenant Greg Lewis, and the engineer, Sergeant George Morris. The only one having remained silent was Air Load Mistress Clarke, for the captain had never even glanced at her, much less encouraged her to take part in the discussion. Used as she was to this treatment, Simoni hated these pre-flight meetings.

With the discussion at an end Captain Travers gave his crew leave to go, but as Simoni reached the door he said, in those curt clipped accents which she knew he kept especially for her,

'Load – you will remain behind.'

Simoni turned, her pulse fluttering. What complaint had he this time? she wondered with a soundless sigh of resignation.

Captain Travers stood in the middle of the room; Simoni halted some distance from him so as to be able to meet his gaze without having to tilt her head right back.

'I trust you've been digesting all I had to say earlier today?'

'Yes, sir.'

'You don't consider me too unreasonable in requesting a snag-free flight tomorrow?'

The sarcasm of the man!

'No, sir.'

'Or too optimistic?'

How she would love to send him a glance that revealed her opinion of him!

'No, sir.'

He moved; this brought him closer to her and so after all she was forced to tilt her head in order to look into his face. An inordinately handsome face, Simoni grudgingly owned, with perfectly-cut features and the sort of noble character lines that only maturity could produce. His mouth was firm yet not too thin, and his thrusting jaw portrayed power rather than aggressiveness. Captain Kent Travers, thirty-five and with thirteen years' service behind him, was in every way a man's man, and despite the fact of his being the most physically attractive male on the station no one considered it strange that he was still a bachelor.

'So you think, sergeant, that by some miracle we might possibly achieve this snag-free flight?'

Simoni wondered what he would say were she to inform him that things had gone wrong only since he became her boss.

'I sincerely hope so, sir.'

He glanced down at her, his piercing grey eyes cold and sternly critical.

'You're the most inefficient A.L.M. I've ever worked with,' he told her cuttingly. 'And I must warn you that I'm coming to the end of my patience.'

Simoni quivered with indignation.

'I would like to point out, sir, that these mishaps aren't always my fault. Some things are out of my con-

6

trol — as for example when the freezing plant failed—'

'Are you making excuses?'

'No – not exactly, but—'

'There is no excuse for inefficiency. Buck your ideas up! Keep your mind off your young man when you're on duty!'

'Oh,' she quivered, 'I never think of—' She stopped, checked by the glint in his eye, and muttered, 'I'm sorry, sir.'

A small uncomfortable silence followed, and then,

'I *expect* a snag-free flight tomorrow, understand?'

'Yes, sir.'

'You may go,' he then said, and thankfully Simoni left the room.

The man had never liked her, she reflected, making her way to the Sergeants' Mess in the opposite block. Even on their first meeting he had treated her with unnecessary curtness and indifference. Then, inexplicably, Simoni had made several minor mistakes, and Captain Travers' admonishments had been far more severe and crushing than would have been the case with her last boss, who in any case had always praised Simoni's efficiency.

Simoni entered the sergeants' bar; none of her friends were there and she made for the ante-room. As she entered several young men looked up.

'Hi, Simoni!'

'Hi!' She moved on, taking possession of a vacant chair by a table at which two of her friends were seated.

'What's up – as if I didn't know?' Air Load Mistress

Linda Pierce glanced perceptively at her. 'That man again, obviously.'

Simoni nodded. 'I detest him! Why was I the unfortunate one chosen for his crew? Why wasn't it one of you?'

'Don't be like that. Why should you wish such ill-luck on your best friends?'

In spite of herself Simoni had to laugh. It was quite impossible not to laugh with Linda; she was so droll and dry.

'Been tearing a strip off you again, has he?' Carole drew on her cigarette and stared at Simoni through the smoke haze.

'He did that earlier. No, he merely asked, with that detestable brand of sarcasm, if it were possible for us to have a trouble-free flight tomorrow.'

Her two friends laughed at this. Simoni glowered at them in turn, but that only served to increase their amusement.

'You've got a thing about him, Simoni. You anticipate trouble.'

Simoni pondered on this, dwelling again on her life before Captain Travers became her superior officer. Captain Holmes was so very different, extending praise where it was due and always being kind and friendly when off duty. He had no need to tell her she was efficient – Simoni knew this. But ill-luck seemed to have dogged her from the first moment of working with Kent Travers and something was always going wrong.

'I think the whole trouble is that he's never really liked me.' Simoni thought about that first meeting – the start Kent gave, and the disbelieving stare, just as if he couldn't take in the evidence of his eyes. His whole manner had been so strange, and with the first words spoken to her Simoni sensed a deep dislike. Yet it seemed a ridiculous conclusion for her to have reached, because there was no valid reason for it.

'What has his liking or disliking to do with it?' Carole shook her head emphatically. 'As I've said, you anticipate trouble; you expect things to go wrong and so of course they do go wrong. From the moment of his coming aboard your aircraft and occupying that awesome left-hand seat you're all of a dither!'

'No such thing! I've been in the Force too long for that!'

'But you've been with Captain Travers only three months.'

Three months . . . it seemed more like three years!

'So many things have gone wrong in that time,' she murmured, speaking her thoughts aloud.

'Only minor things, though. You worry unnecessarily. We all make mistakes at times; none of us is infallible.'

'They are minor mistakes, I know, but they seem to annoy him out of all proportion.' With conviction of his dislike slowly impressing itself on her, Simoni's confidence was to some degree undermined and in consequence the small slips she made seemed to become more numerous.

'Because he's a perfectionist,' declared Linda. 'Good thing he's a confirmed bachelor; a woman's life would be hell with a man like that around all the time.'

'Oh, I don't know. . . .' Carole's eyes became dreamy. 'He's certainly a stunner. I don't think I'd mind at all being married to him.'

'You wouldn't mind—!' Simoni could only stare. 'You're quite mad, Carole!'

Carole shrugged. 'Everyone to his or her own taste. I like the masterful type myself.'

'He'd be more than masterful,' interposed Linda in emphatic tones. 'He'd be downright domineering.'

'You're dead right about that,' was Simoni's heart-felt response as she leant back in her chair, relaxed. 'If you're so keen on the man, Carole, perhaps we could arrange a swop. I'm sure he'd be only too relieved to have another Load Mistress on his crew.'

'You know that's not possible. You're stuck with him, Simoni, so you might as well become resigned.' Linda glanced sympathetically at her friend.

'I was happy in the Force till he came here.' Simoni gave a deep sigh. 'However, it's only another six months, thank heaven!'

'Six months? Is that all you've still to serve? How time does fly.'

'You haven't had the results of your final exams yet?' asked Carole interestedly.

'Not yet.' Simoni had been studying hard at the R.A.F. school, having become interested in geology during her many flights to the Middle East. She had also made a special study of oil and hoped at the end of her service to obtain a post with an oil company, for this would take her to the places in the East which she had come to love. 'I shall be bitterly disappointed if I haven't passed.'

'You will have,' Linda asserted firmly. 'You work so hard you must succeed. I wish I had your energy.' Simoni said nothing and Linda added, rather hesitantly, 'What about Matthew? Aren't you going to marry him?'

Simoni shook her head. 'It's all very platonic on both sides. Matthew has no interest in marriage and neither have I.'

Carole looked at her, examining her face intently.

'Don't know how any man could be platonic with you,' she said at length. 'You're too attractive.'

Simoni blushed and told her friend to cut out the flattery, at which Carole only laughed and said,

'If I had that face and those eyes I'd be employing them in the business of procuring myself a rich husband, and to the devil with a career.'

Before Simoni could find a suitable retort to that the three girls were joined by John and Frank, two Air Load Masters, who sat down uninvited.

'Women's talk – or can we intrude?'

'You already have.' Linda eyed John with a knowing stare. 'News – it's written in capitals all over your rugged manly face. Who are you intending to slander this time?'

John wagged a forefinger at her. 'Now, now, don't be bitchy, Linda. You know full well that if it wasn't for Johnny Boy you'd never hear anything!'

'Just how do you do it?' Simoni wanted to know, leaning forward and resting her elbows on the table so that she could cup her chin in her hands. 'You seem to smell out the gossip.'

Assuming a hurt expression, John said,

'If that's how you're all going to treat me then I'll take my news somewhere else. Come on, Frank, these women have no sense of gratitude—'

'Wait.' Carole held out her packet of cigarettes. 'It's only those two. I'm always ready for a bit of gossip.

Who is it?'

Mollified, John sat down again, and helped himself to a cigarette.

'Captain Travers.'

Simoni turned her head and looked at him.

'Captain Travers?'

'So that's made you take notice. I've still a mind to keep you guessing.'

'Don't be childish, John,' cut in Carole. 'Out with it – you know you're dying to impart your knowledge. What's Simoni's boss been doing?'

'It's what he's *going* to do. He's leaving the service.'

'He is?' Eagerness in Simoni's tones. 'When?'

'How can he leave?' began Linda impulsively, then stopped, nodding. Carole said,

'Of course he can leave; he's an officer. It's only the ragtag and bobtail like us who have to work out our time.' She glanced at John. 'I can't imagine him anywhere else but in the captain's awesome left-hand seat. What's happened?'

'Come into a fortune – an uncle in America. No family, so he's left his millions to the captain.'

'Millions? Don't talk rot.'

John shrugged. 'Must be a nice princely sum, because it's rumoured he's negotiating for the purchase of an air charter company – so he won't exactly be giving up his flying, although I suppose he'll employ pilots for most of the flying and do the administration work himself from his sumptuous office in Nicosia.'

'Nicosia?' Simoni loved Cyprus. She could never live there, of course, because of work permits, but were it at all possible that delectable island was where she would like to settle. 'Is it a Cypriot company he's buying?'

'No, it's an English company but with offices also in Nicosia. Knowing the captain, I expect he'll be at Nicosia more than he's in England. He happens to be a sun-lover.'

'When is he leaving?' Simoni asked again, and both her friends laughed at her eagerness.

'In about six months or so – at least, that's what I've heard.'

Simoni's face fell. 'What damnable luck!' she exploded.

John looked hard at her. 'Still having trouble with him?'

'It looks as if I'll have trouble with him right till the end!'

'Poor Simoni.' John paused and then added teasingly, 'A long flight tomorrow. Plenty of time in which to get his back up, I reckon.'

'And plenty of time for things to go wrong,' was the swift and rather dismal rejoinder. Something was bound to go wrong, she thought with a fitful sigh.

'I wonder why he doesn't like you?' mused Carole thoughtfully.

'I expect he has his reasons,' Simoni almost snapped. 'With everybody else he's as friendly as can be when off duty. The men always call him by his Christian name, and the other loads call him "boss" in the most casual way.'

'So could you call him "boss", but you never do.' Linda told her, but Simoni shook her head.

'I always feel I daren't – that he'd pounce on me if I did.'

'Know what I've heard?' said John casually, staring

13

hard at Simoni again.

'There's more?' Carole seized eagerly on that. 'Come on, then.'

'Simoni happens to look almost exactly like his fiancée—'

'His fiancée? He hasn't got a fiancée.' Linda glanced inquiringly at John, waiting for an explanation.

'His ex-fiancée, I should have said. She let him down, apparently – and that could be the reason he took an instant dislike to Simoni.'

'You mean – Simoni has a double?'

'I wouldn't know about that, but this chap who was telling me about it remarked on the likeness. Simoni has the same colouring – gingery hair and dark eyes—'

'What do you mean, gingery?' interrupted Carole with swift indignation. 'Simoni's hair's what is termed as chestnut.'

John shrugged. 'Looks ginger to me – darkish ginger, granted—'

'All right,' cut in Simoni. 'In what other way do I resemble his ex-fiancée?' She was thoughtful, remembering the sudden start Kent Travers had given on being introduced to her, and his subsequent curtness and indifference.

'Same features and build. Slim and dainty, if you know what I mean?'

'I can't imagine Captain Travers bothering with women,' mused Linda. 'I always considered him to be a confirmed bachelor.'

'He is now. This happened some years ago.'

'You said she let him down. How?'

'Well, you know what it's like with men in the service. They're away a lot. She amused herself with others, it seems – and her escapades came to Kent's ears. He chucked her, and from all accounts he's never looked at another woman since.'

'If that's the reason for his dislike of me, then he's even more horrid than I thought.' But at least it provided an explanation for her boss's attitude towards her, thought Simoni. 'Where's this girl now?'

'Married, quite happily from all accounts.'

'It doesn't seem to be worrying him overmuch. He appears to be quite recovered from any hurt he might have suffered.'

'As I said, it happened a long while ago.'

At five o'clock the following morning Simoni, the only female member of the crew, was aboard the aircraft carrying out, with the stewards, her pre-flight duties of checking the seating arrangements for the passengers coming aboard. Having satisfied herself that all seats were serviceable and harnesses fixed she then checked all the food as it came aboard from the in-flight catering unit and then, an hour and a half after Simoni and the other members of the crew had reported for duty, the passengers arrived. Simoni checked out with the movements clerks, and the police, that the number of passengers tallied with the head check, and she received the passengers' manifests which she put safely away in her file. Simoni checked out a small piece of priority hand-freight, which she stowed away on a shelf in the galley.

Once the passengers were all seated it was her task to brief them while the flight-deck crew were preparing to start the engines.

She bade them good morning, and welcomed them aboard the aircraft, giving the name of their captain, and her own name as well.

'Over the initial part of the flight,' Simoni continued, 'we shall be cruising at an altitude of thirty thousand feet, and the weather is expected to be good. In the unlikely event of an emergency please take notification of myself or any other crew member. The crew are about to start the engines, so will you please bring your seats into the upright position? I hope you have a pleasant flight.'

Simoni then put back her head-set and spoke to the flight-deck crew, finalizing all preparations for the take-off run.

At the top of climb she went round, making sure the passengers were comfortable, then instructed the stewards to issue them with food and drinks.

Just before landing at Akrotiri, in Cyprus, where some of the passengers were leaving the aircraft and others coming aboard, Simoni called one of the stewards to her and handed him the priority package.

'This is to be left at the base,' she said. 'Will you see to it?'

'Yes, okay.' He put the package into his pocket. But a few minutes after leaving Akrotiri he came to her in the galley, and she saw at once that something was wrong.

'Sergeant,' he began hesitantly, 'I've – I've forgotten to leave the package—'

'You've—?' Simoni's heart turned a somersault. 'No ... it isn't possible!'

'I'm afraid so.' He handed it to her. She looked at

the red label: 'Priority One, Akrotiri. . . .'

A snag-free flight. . . . The other minor snags were nothing to this, she thought, her heart turning right over again. The steward had to return to his duties and Simoni was left with the package in her hand, terrified of informing the captain. Yet every moment was taking them farther away and at last she put on her head-set and spoke, her voice husky because of her apprehension.

'Load Mistress – Captain. . . .'

'Go ahead, Load Mistress.'

'I'm terribly sorry, but – but I have some bad news—'

'Bad news?' Swift and sharp the two words came and Simoni swallowed hard, for her throat felt blocked.

'I have a piece of Priority One freight for Akrotiri which – which we forgot to off-load.'

'*What!*'

Simoni jumped as the voice thundered in her head.

'I'm sorry, sir. . . .'

Her face was white when he came into the galley a few seconds later. And all she could do was stand there, quite unable to speak, even had she been given the opportunity of doing so. The captain himself was livid, and the fact that the steward came in, admitting the blame, made no difference whatsoever. Simoni was the sergeant in charge, the stewards being her subordinates. The steward was ordered out and Simoni again received the full brunt of the captain's fury.

'You realize we'll have to go back!' he thundered.

Miserably she nodded, managing to look up at last,

her eyes far too bright.

'I'm so sorry—'

'Sorry! You're always sorry – and for God's sake don't start to cry! That sort of feminine self-pity I couldn't stand!'

'I – I wasn't—' But Simoni stopped, for tears were actually blurring her vision. To her relief he stalked out before she disgraced herself in front of him.

Not only had they to turn round and go back to off-load the freight but they had also to uplift fuel, to compensate for what they had lost. This naturally caused some delay which, Simoni surmised, would surely serve to increase the captain's fury, and the idea of going on to the flight deck with the men's coffee quite dismayed her. But although the stewards served the passengers it was the Load Mistress's duty to see to the requirements of the crew.

After serving their coffee she asked about the meal.

'Are you eating first, sir?' Naturally both pilots could not eat together, nor must they eat the same food as each other. This latter was a precaution against food poisoning, which, although a highly improbable eventuality, was just possible.

'No, I'll eat later,' he snapped, and Simoni made her departure without looking at him, for she knew instinctively that his expression would set her nerves quivering all over again.

On arrival at Muharraq Simoni took the passengers to Britannia House, the Royal Air Force transit hotel, and then her duties were over, except of course for ordering refreshments for the crew. Simoni had previously collected their money for this and after ordering the sandwiches she went into the bar to order the beer.

'All different brands,' she said, forcing herself to smile in response to the greeting from the friendly Bahraini barman.

'We've all the others, but no Ansdale,' he said brightly. 'What will you have instead?'

'No Ansdale?' It needed only this, she thought dejectedly. 'That was for the captain.'

The barman shrugged. 'He'll drink something else, surely?'

A great sigh escaped her. 'I expect so. Make it Daresburg, then.'

'What's this?' demanded Kent when it was put before him. 'You know what I drink.'

'I'm sorry, sir,' she said in a voice of resignation. 'But they didn't have your brand,' and she just had to add, on seeing his glowering expression, 'I can't be blamed for that, sir.'

They were on the ground now, and there was a different atmosphere among the crew, a freer relationship.

She sat with the men, chatting to Greg and Miles, whom she now called by their Christian names, as was customary when they were all off duty. They in turn addressed the captain as Kent, although this fraternization was frowned on by the high-ups in the Air Force. However, the captains were usually good sports and Kent Travers was no exception.

After a while another crew came in off a different aircraft and Simoni's face broke into a swift smile as she recognized Captain Roy Holmes.

'Curly!' she exclaimed impulsively, using his nickname. 'How nice to see you!' She was aware of the swift glance of Kent Travers, and the slight lifting of an eyebrow at her familiarity with her former superior officer.

'Simoni!' Roy strode across the room and joined them. 'This is a most pleasant surprise. My, but you grow more lovely every day!'

'You're still the Force's greatest flatterer,' she admonished laughingly.

Kent's interest was still evident; Simoni was only human and the opportunity of allowing Kent to witness the sort of relationship existing between her and her old boss naturally afforded her extreme satisfaction.

Roy had turned to the captain.

'Kent – hello! So it's you who has my little Load Mistress, damn you! The best in the Force, she is!'

'Indeed?' sardonically and with a sideways glance at Simoni which brought the colour to her cheeks. 'You must possess some capacity for bringing out the best in your crew – a capacity which I obviously lack. I must have the benefit of your advice some time.'

Simoni set her teeth. Why must he always be so sarcastic?

'I don't get you?' Roy looked blank.

'Captain Travers doesn't share your opinion of me,' said Simoni, gathering courage from the presence of Roy. '*He* thinks I'm the worst in the Force.'

'What! I'll not have that – never!' Roy glanced from Simoni to Kent. 'You'd better explain?'

An awkward silence fell on the group. To Simoni's surprise Kent displayed a reluctance to speak of her shortcomings before the others.

The silence was ended by George who, glancing across the room, saw the engineer from the other aircraft.

'Jeff! I haven't seen you for years! Come on over here and join us!'

'George!' Jeff came striding across the room and sat down at their table. 'Where have you been all this time?' He glanced round, saw they were all strangers except Roy and turned again to George, who instantly began the introductions.

'What are you doing now?' George wanted to know, and Jeff gave a grimace, mentioning the name of his aircraft and then adding,

'Bag of old iron, it is. Blooming old Proteus engine, spitting out nails all over the place.'

The two engineers then started talking engines; this was tolerated for a few minutes and then, after deprecating glances had passed between the others, Miles said,

'That's enough. Come on, Eng, close the hangar doors!'

'Aw, up your nose!'

The incident had brought back a lightheartedness to the company and the two captains forgot all about their previous conversation. Later, Barbara Wood, the Load Mistress from the other aircraft, joined them and she and Simoni fell into conversation on their own.

At last, thoroughly tired out by the long and not very pleasant flight, Simoni interrupted the men's conversation to say good night.

Roy looked up. 'Going, Simoni? Already?'

'I'm very tired, Curly. See you tomorrow. Barbara says you'll be on the island for a week?'

'That's right – and so will you, Kent tells me, so I must take you out. How about tomorrow evening? Dinner at the Gulf?'

'That'll be lovely.' A fluttering glance at Kent and then, 'It'll be like old times!'

'Sure it will.' A small pause and then, 'Perhaps I'll book you right now for every evening – before I'm baulked by some of these young gallants here. Every evening, Simoni?'

She shook her head. 'Barbara and I are doing some exploring and we might not be back, so I'll not commit myself.'

'Certainly you'll be back. However, we'll talk about it some other time. Come to think, you do look all in. Off you go, my dear, and get a good night's rest.' He spoke in the old way, just as if she were still on his crew, his eyes rather anxiously fixed on her face. 'Yes, off you go. I'll see you at breakfast. Good night, Simoni.'

'Good night, Curly.' She said good night again to the others and then pointedly, as she looked across at Kent, 'Good night, sir.'

'Good night,' he returned, using the customary clipped and curt tones which he kept for her alone.

CHAPTER TWO

THE intense blue of the coral seas was at times dazzling to the eyes and after coming out of the water Simoni put on her dark glasses. Her body was already brown, for she always made the most of the sun in the exotic places she was fortunate enough to visit.

'Gosh, that was lovely!' Barbara sat down, having stayed in the water a little longer than Simoni. 'It's so warm in there.'

'Of course. Coral wouldn't grow if it wasn't.'

Barbara towelled her arms and said, curiously,

'You seem to be extraordinarily knowledgeable about such things.'

'I've been studying geology. I'm expecting the results of my final exams any day now.'

'Geology?' Barbara frowned in a rather pained sort of way. 'That seems an odd sort of subject to study. Will you be able to use it when you leave the service?'

'I hope I shall. I want to work for an oil company.'

'Work where the money is, eh?'

'I suppose the money does come into it,' was Simoni's frank admission. 'But I also want to enjoy my job. Nothing is more soul-destroying than to be forced to work at something you don't like.'

Barbara threw down the towel, spreading it out so that she could lie on it.

'I expect I shall end up in an office, or some other

23

place as uninteresting and confined. The service spoils you for settling down.'

'I agree. This worried me and that's why I decided to take advantage of the educational facilities offered.' Simoni lay back, resting her head on her clasped hands. The sun was hot on her legs and body and the sand beneath her was warm. Not far below the sand was the coral, a beautiful sample of which Simoni had collected on a previous visit to the island of Bahrain.

'Tell me about the coral.' Barbara rolled on to her stomach, exposing her back to the sun. 'It's not exactly a rock, is it?'

'Yes, it's a rock—' Simoni paused, then said, 'It's rather complicated.'

'I expect it is – but can't you explain in words of one syllable?'

Simoni laughed. 'Well, the rock is formed by the hard skeletons of coral and many other tiny organisms the successive generations of which grow upwards and outwards – because of the continuous search for food. These spreading growths gradually take the shape of the lovely tree-like formations which we usually associ-ate with coral – although there are many other equally beautiful formations, like the brain coral, for example, and the stag's horn coral.'

Barbara was probing into the sand and after a while she said,

'Is this coral under here alive?'

Simoni shook her head. 'Coral can't survive the con-ditions that exist above low-tide level, so any reefs found above sea level are dead.'

'But if they can't live above low-tide level then how did this coral get here in the first place?'

'It would have been formed under the sea and then uplifted by earth movements – these movements are going on all the time, but they're so slight that we don't notice them.'

Barbara looked a trifle confused. 'You just said the sea must be warm, but if they only grow deep down—'

'They don't grow deep down. One of the necessities for the formation of coral is the existence of a platform not too far below sea level. The waters are warm, and they always have to be clear, and that's why you get coral seas only where rivers aren't carrying mud and silt into the sea.'

'That means desert conditions, then – like we have here on this island?'

'That's the general rule, yes.'

'What about coral islands – I mean, can a whole island be made up of coral?'

'Of course, and very attractive these islands are. A soil is formed with the result that you get vivid greens all over the place, and of course the coconut palm one always associates with a coral island – and the waters round are, of course, warm and clear, otherwise the island would never have come into existence in the first place.'

Barbara sat up, looking at Simoni with admiration not untinged with wonderment.

'It's absolutely fascinating! Why didn't I think of studying geology?'

'People don't really go into it – which is such a pity, because life certainly takes on a tremendous interest. After all, the rocks are the basis of life. Practically every single thing we use comes initially from the rocks.'

Simoni laughed at Barbara's disbelieving expression. 'Where else can things come from?'

'But . . . the meat we eat . . .?'

'Cattle can't exist without food, and their food comes from the soil. And,' she added laughingly, 'the soil is made from the rocks.'

'Well,' exclaimed Barbara, shaking her head in a dazed sort of way, 'to think I never gave such matters a single thought until now!'

Simoni laughed again; her laugh rang out, like a silver bell shedding music in the clear warm air.

'What was that for?' inquired a masculine voice, and both girls turned their heads.

'Curly!' It was Barbara who spoke, for Simoni was looking at Kent, standing there clad only in trunks, his body the colour of an Arab's. Thick hair covered his chest and legs and the lower parts of his arms. He was looking down at Simoni, his grey eyes examining her scantily-clad figure without any hint of restraint. Simoni blushed and glanced away. His presence displeased her, for although with Roy she could be relaxed and free from inhibitions, with Kent she had always to remember that he was her superior. Assuredly he would mar the open friendly atmosphere which would have resulted had Roy been on his own.

'May we join you?' asked Roy, smiling down at Simoni.

'Of course.'

The two men carried towels; these they spread on the sand and then sat down on them.

'What was that delightful laugh for?' Roy asked again, turning to Simoni.

'Simoni was telling me about the formation of coral,'

Barbara informed him before Simoni could speak. 'And she was laughing at my expression.' Barbara smiled at her boss and he responded. Simoni felt mean for envying Barbara – after all, Simoni had had a fair share of Roy – but she did envy Barbara, wished she herself were working with Roy still, instead of with the arrogant and infuriatingly sarcastic Kent Travers.

'Ah, yes.' Roy glanced at Simoni. 'You're still studying geology?'

'I've recently taken my final exams, but I haven't yet heard how I've got on.' She caught Kent's expression as she spoke, noting the momentary flicker of interest before he resumed his more familiar manner of bored indifference which for the first time strangely disconcerted her.

Roy, following the direction of her gaze, lapsed into a thoughtful silence for a moment and then said,

'You're sure to pass, Simoni. You worked very hard indeed on that course.'

'Simoni's hoping to get a post with an oil company,' submitted Barbara, and Roy nodded.

'That should be interesting. You want to continue travelling, I presume?'

'For a little while longer, yes.'

'Well, I wish you luck, Simoni. I sincerely hope you pass your exams and, having done so, that you manage to get the post you desire.'

'Thank you, Curly. We must keep in touch, so that I can let you know how I go on.'

'I'm going in the sea again,' said Barbara after a while. 'Anyone coming with me?'

'Yes, I will.' Roy got up and a few seconds later Simoni found herself alone with Kent, recalling somewhat ruefully that on all other occasions when she had been alone with him it was for the express purpose of being called over the coals for something. No reprimand was expected this time; nevertheless she suffered the same discomfiture and fervently hoped the other two would not stay out there too long, for the silence was already producing a strained atmosphere between Kent and herself. At last she just had to break it, saying in a forced and somewhat hesitant voice,

'You've been in the water, I notice. Isn't it marvellous?'

'Most pleasant, yes.'

'We're lucky to be here for a week.'

'Are we?' He glanced casually at her, unmoved by her attempts at friendliness. 'I know of better places.'

'Obviously there are better places.' Was he thinking of Cyprus? she wondered, reflecting on what John had said about the fortune he had inherited and the charter company he was hoping to buy. Simoni rather thought Kent would make his home in Cyprus, building himself one of those magnificent white villas which were gradually springing up on the island. Some were designed on the pseudo-Cypriot style, and very attractive they were, with their wide arches and pillared patios and terraces spilling over with exotic flowers. How lucky he was, she thought – and how *unlucky* were the poor Cypriot servants he would in all probability employ. For a man with so scathing and sarcastic a tongue as that of Kent Travers would assuredly be a tyrant to work for. 'What I really meant was that we're lucky to be able to bathe in the sea without feeling cold, as one would in England,' Simoni added as she realized Kent was actually expecting some further comment from her. 'I wouldn't like to live permanently in England.'

'But you'll have to, some day, surely?'

She nodded, saying rather flatly,

'I expect so, yes. But if I get the job I want I'll be in the East for a while.'

'As long as the job lasts, you mean?'

'That's right. With this sort of job you can't say whether it will be permanent or not.'

'You do realize that men are usually employed as geologists?'

Her little pointed chin lifted; it was an unconscious gesture and she was at a loss as to the reason for the sudden glint that entered her companion's eyes.

'Women can do most jobs just as well as men. Employers are coming round to admitting this, and about time too!' She was staring out across the bay; two crab-plovers skimmed the sea, then swooped into the air, flying into the sun. In the far distance at the water's edge she could just discern two dusky fishermen dragging along their net close to the shore, trapping the small fish left by the ebb-tide in the shallows.

'Most jobs?' Kent regarded her sardonically from under half-closed lids. Simoni flushed, reading his thoughts. They were off duty now, and although it was still imprudent she just had to say,

'I haven't been very lucky since I began working with you. With Captain Holmes things always seemed to go right.'

'So it would appear. As I remarked, I must seek his advice.'

She bit her lip, angry with herself for providing an opening like that.

'I'm really very sorry,' she said, and meant it. 'I can quite see how annoying these little snags are—'

'Little snags?' The captain's brows shot up. 'You consider our having to return to Cyprus as a little snag?'

'I gave the package to one of the stewards – which was quite in order. It was just my infernal luck that he should take it off and then bring it back. It was in his pocket all the time.'

'You were in charge. It was your duty to see that the package was off-loaded.'

No excuse. Kent Travers would never excuse a mistake like that. He'd consider it as gross inefficiency and, as he had so recently remarked, there was no excuse for inefficiency. Simoni sighed audibly; Kent gave a short laugh and told her not to be sorry for herself.

'I'm not!' she flashed, indifferent to the probable consequences. 'I'm never sorry for myself!'

'Women,' he returned after a rather ominous silence, 'are invariably sorry for themselves. They make the stupidest mistakes, and on being reprimanded they resort to self-pity, adopting an air of martyrdom – which of course is designed to make the one who's reprimanded them consider himself a heel.'

'I presume,' said Simoni in a quivering voice, 'that you're referring exclusively to women you've had under your command.'

He inclined his head in a gesture of agreement.

'My experience of women comes mainly from those I've had under my command.'

Simoni did not comment. She was musing on what John had said about Kent's having at one time been engaged to be married. For some reason Simoni gained the impression that although he had been engaged, his relationship with his fiancée wasn't quite what Simoni herself would have desired. When she became engaged Simoni knew she would want a close and intimate spiritual and mental relationship with her fiancé. This would be quite impossible with a cold, austere man like Kent Travers, and while Simoni could not excuse his fiancée's conduct in keeping company with other men in his absence, she at the same time felt the girl was lucky to have escaped marriage with so unpredictable and sarcastic a man as Captain Kent Travers.

She glanced up as the other two came out of the sea, but her attention was drawn again to the fishermen. They had waded out with the net, but now they brought it in with a wide flourish, and bent down to take out the fish which they then tossed into a basket. The men's bodies, lean and strong from hard living, were naked except for coloured loincloths and scarves wound round their heads. They began dragging again and the fish, coming to the surface, were leaping from the water like birds.

'Have you seen those fish?' exclaimed Barbara on coming out of the water, and, when Simoni nodded, 'How they jump!' Barbara flopped down, sighing contentedly, 'This is the life for me!'

Roy also lowered himself on to the sands and dried his legs.

'How about having lunch together?' he suggested, and Simoni glanced swiftly at Kent. Had the suggestion placed him in an awkward position? If so he hid his annoyance remarkably well as he said,

'A good idea, Roy. Have you any suggestions as to a place?'

'The Moon Plaza Hotel,' returned Roy. 'They serve superb food.'

They took a taxi, driving into Manama, but immediately after lunch they separated, as the girls wanted to do some shopping.

'I must have souvenirs,' said Barbara. 'Something local.'

'I'm afraid you won't find much in the way of local craft,' Kent informed her. 'Practically everything's imported from our own country, or the U.S. and Japan.'

'Really? Don't the natives make pots and baskets and things?'

'Pearls are about the only local products you'll find, Barbara,' said Roy. 'However, you two have a look round, if that's what you want. If I don't see you before, Simoni, I'll meet you in the bar – at the Britt, of course – at seven-thirty. All right?'

She smiled and nodded. 'I'll be there.'

'What have you got that I haven't?' Barbara wanted to know a few minutes later as they were strolling round the streets of Manama, looking at the shops. 'Curly never takes me out.'

For a moment Simoni could think of no reply to that, but as Barbara obviously expected one she said that perhaps it was because Roy was her boss.

'Did he not take you out when he was your boss?'

Reluctantly Simoni nodded. 'Yes – yes, he did.'

Barbara laughed at Simoni's expression.

'Don't take it to heart, Simoni. I don't really mind. I've got a nice boy-friend at home and he'd be mad anyway, if he thought I'd go about with anyone else. I met him only five months ago and he can't wait for me to come out. He hates the idea of my being surrounded by all these men.' Barbara paused, glancing sideways at Simoni. 'Haven't you a boy-friend?'

'Yes – sort of.'

'Sort of?'

'We're not serious – just good friends.'

'Not very satisfactory, is it?'

'It suits us.'

They stopped to look at the pearls, lovely specimens of every shape and size, brought from the ocean bed by the pearl divers of Bahrain.

'The colour!' exclaimed Barbara. 'How beautiful it is!'

'Bahrain pearls have always been far superior to others because of the numerous fresh-water springs in the seas around it.'

'Are there fresh-water springs in the sea?' Barbara stared disbelievingly at Simoni.

'Round here there are, yes. Divers go down with skin bags and fill them.'

After buying a string of pearls each they visited the Gold Market, coming away with filigree brooches and in Barbara's case, a fine gold bracelet.

'I've thoroughly enjoyed that,' said Simoni on returning to Britt House. 'I'm glad I met you, Barbara.'

'Same here. It's not much fun strolling about on one's own.'

A few hours later Simoni and Roy were entering through the beautiful high glass doors of the Gulf Hotel, with above their heads the vast awning studded with multi-coloured lights. Simoni was in a thin cocktail dress of fine white cotton trimmed with delicate embroidery round the waist and hem. Her arms were bare and brown, her hair newly-washed and shining. It was one of those occasions when she felt she looked her very best. Roy wore thin slacks and a long-sleeved shirt, and of course, a tie.

He had chatted in the taxi about nothing in particular, but once in the bar at the hotel he said guardedly,

'You don't appear to be as happy as you were, Simoni?'

She paused, taking up her glass from the table. Roy had broached a delicate subject, for neither he nor she should discuss Captain Travers. At length she smiled and said,

'You spoiled me for any other boss.'

'Clever . . . and diplomatic – just as it should be, of course. Nevertheless, I'm a trifle worried about you, my dear. Perhaps I'm out of place in the Force, but I do worry about people.' He looked at her, searchingly. 'Why should Kent think you're inefficient—?'

'He didn't say that.'

'He didn't say anything, but you did. I gathered he isn't altogether pleased with you?'

A deep sigh escaped her.

'I've been going through a bad patch lately, Roy. For instance, yesterday we left Cyprus without off-loading a piece of priority freight. We had to turn round and go back.'

'You did?' Roy's eyes widened. 'He slated you? – but of course he did, and, Simoni,' added Roy with emphasis, 'so would I have done.'

She nodded in agreement. 'It was sheer bad luck,

34

though. I gave it to one of the stewards and he forgot to leave it.' She fell silent, sipping her drink reflectively. 'Naturally he was furious, and I don't blame him. I've made several mistakes lately – since working with Captain Travers, that is.'

'It's a pity. I like Kent Travers enormously, and though you might not believe it, he's always been popular with his crews. With you, though, his coolness was very noticeable. That's why I decided to go into it.' He paused a moment, seeming to be interested only in the mosaic prettily displayed on the table top. But at last he looked up. 'Is there anything I can do to help?' he asked.

'It's kind of you to offer your help, Curly, but I don't really think there's anything you can do.' She could scarcely mention that Kent had disliked her from the start, and much less that his dislike probably stemmed from the fact of her resemblance to his ex-fianceé. 'In any case,' she went on, giving him a smile, 'my position isn't all that bad. Captain Travers isn't vindictive – I do hope I haven't conveyed an idea like that?'

'No, of course you haven't.' He stopped as the waiter came to their table with the menu. Having made their choice they were told the meal would be ready in about ten minutes' time. 'You're leaving soon, anyway, aren't you?'

Simoni nodded, then said, curiously, 'Did you know it was rumoured Captain Travers was intending to resign?'

'It's no rumour, but fact. Lucky blighter, he's inherited a fortune.'

'He's buying an air charter company, so I believe.'

'That's right. Just the sort of business I'd like to be in when I leave.'

Presently the waiter reappeared and they were conducted into the restaurant and to a table by the window where they could look out on to the gardens with their palm trees and beautifully-illuminated pool in which some of the guests were swimming.

In between courses Roy and Simoni danced to the music provided by the combo – the Italian group which had been at the hotel for several years.

'Thanks, Curly, for a wonderful evening.' Simoni turned to him as they stepped out of the taxi on returning to the Britt. 'I've had a lovely time.'

'Thank you, Simoni. You're always so nice to be with.'

He glanced past her and she turned. Kent had been out with Miles and they too were alighting from a taxi.

'Hello,' said Miles, and then, with an appreciative whistle, 'Simoni, you look stunning! Come, let me buy you a drink.'

Kent looked at her, in a searching way as if he would ascertain the truth of Miles's enthusiastic declaration. His manner disconcerted her, in a far different way from anything she had hitherto experienced, and she swiftly dropped her eyes, conscious of the colour rising in her cheeks.

'I – I think I'll go to bed, Miles,' she began, when he interrupted her.

'Bed at this time? What on earth for?'

'It's late—'

'Nonsense!' he retorted, and with a shrug and a rather forced little laugh she accompanied him and the two captains into the bar.

36

CHAPTER THREE

A MONTH later Simoni was again in the squadron crew room at R.A.F. Sedenlowe, listening to Captain Travers making his final plans for another long-range strategic flight to the Gulf. As before he told Simoni to remain behind when the others had left.

'We seem to have had better luck lately,' he said. 'Can this be kept up, do you think?'

'I'm hoping it will be kept up, sir.'

'I'm not expecting to have to turn back for anything this time.'

She gave a little trembling sigh. There was no necessity for that reminder, she thought, saying with an edge of indignation to her voice,

'I never make the same mistake twice, sir!'

Kent's piercing grey eyes took on the faintest glint of amusement. Simoni was surprised, but unexpectant. What he had to say would not be amusing, that was for sure.

'I do grant you that, Load. But unfortunately you have the extraordinary ability of finding new ones to make.'

She coloured up, clenching her fists. His eyes moved, resting on her hands. Slowly she straightened out her fingers, pressing them against the sides of her skirt.

'Captain Travers,' she said quiveringly at length, 'you've blamed me for several things which were totally out of my control – I'm sorry to remind you of this,' she added hastily as his expression darkened, 'but

37

in self-defence I feel I must draw your attention to it.'

Somehow Simoni knew that thrust had gone home, though she knew too that the captain naturally would not admit to any injustice on his part.

'You're impertinent!' he snapped, then added, 'As for this attitude of self-pity—'

'It's not! I said "self-defence—"' She was cut short by the crack of the captain's hand on the desk.

'Don't interrupt me when I'm speaking!' Simoni averted her head, but remained silent. The captain kept her standing there for what seemed an unconscionable length of time before he gave her permission to go.

'Phew!' Simoni uttered the gasp of relief almost before the door had closed behind her. 'The sooner I'm out of this place the better I shall feel!'

She was now off duty and at three o'clock that afternoon she had to attend for an interview at an office in London where she would meet a representative of the oil company for which she hoped to work.

Clad neatly but attractively in a plain blue suit, she presented herself promptly and was shown into a sumptuous office where were seated two men, one elderly, and the other about ten years older than Simoni. The interview lasted half an hour. She would shortly receive a letter, Simoni was told, and in the ordinary way this would have meant a period of anxious waiting. But Bill Foden, the younger man present at the interview, followed her out and invited her to have tea with him, adding with a smile,

'We might as well take this opportunity of getting acquainted, Miss Clarke, because we shall undoubtedly

38

be working together in the future.'

'We shall?' She looked up at him and smiled. 'I've got the post?'

'Not officially, but – yes, you can be sure you've got it.'

'That's wonderful!' she breathed. 'Thank you, Mr. Foden, for telling me. Yes, I'd very much like to have tea with you.'

They went into a restaurant, and over their tea Bill Foden talked about his work with the oil company, and Simoni learned that among other things she would be making flights, with Bill, over the desert, carrying out periodic aerial surveys.

'You've landed it,' exclaimed Linda when she and Simoni met in the W.A.A.F. sergeants' coffee room later in the day. 'I can see it in your face! You look exactly the same as when you learned you'd passed your final exams!'

'I have to wait for a letter, but Bill – Mr. Foden – that's the man I'll be working with most of the time, told me the job was mine.'

'Lucky you!' A small pause and then, 'Bill ... you're soon on Christian name terms, aren't you? How come?'

'He took me out to tea.' A faint flush had spread over Simoni's face and her friend said curiously,

'Attractive, is he?'

Simoni nodded, frankly admitting that Bill Foden was extraordinarily attractive.

'Fair hair and blue eyes,' she added reflectively. 'Brown and big and with a nice sincere sort of expression. Very pleasant after—' She broke off and her colour heightened. Linda grinned as she said,

'After the sarcastic and austere Kent Travers, eh?'

Simoni nodded and smiled. 'A very different boss he'll make – Bill, I mean. Life should be most pleasant again once I've said good-bye to the captain for the last time.'

'You could meet him in Civvy Street, you know.'

'Heaven forbid! No, Linda, don't even mention such a possibility. When I leave here I hope never to set eyes on Kent Travers again as long as I live!'

'You certainly dislike him, don't you, Simoni?'

'So would you if you worked under him.'

'Well, there's no fear of that, fortunately, because he'll be leaving at about the same time as you.'

The flight to the Gulf began in rough weather, but as they neared Cyprus all was smooth again. On leaving the island Simoni took out the food from the deep freeze and instructed the stewards to begin preparing the next meal. Meanwhile she went along to the flight deck to see which pilot intended eating first.

'I am,' said Miles. 'Have you chicken?' Simoni nodded and Miles glanced at Kent. 'Do you want the chicken, sir?'

Shaking his head, Kent turned to Simoni. 'What else have you?'

'Gammon steaks.'

'Gammon will do.'

As usual the stewards saw to the needs of the passengers while Simoni looked after the crew. A couple of minutes after the captain had been served he strode into the galley where Simoni was busy making the coffee.

'I asked for gammon,' he snapped, and Simoni

blinked at him, bewildered.

'You have gammon. . . .' Her voice faded. Kent had the container in his hand and she saw the chicken, which of course he was not allowed to eat.

'The – the code must have been wrong,' she faltered, quite unable to believe another mistake had occurred. It was too mortifying. 'The containers are coded, as you know, sir.' He also knew that the normal procedure was to heat the food and deliver it to the consumer with the container still sealed, so all Simoni had to go by was the code written on the lid of each container. 'I saved you the – I saved you what I believed to be the gammon.'

'Saved?' He looked sharply at her. 'You mean there isn't any more?'

'No – no,' she stammered, her nerves fluttering as she realized there was nothing very substantial at all to offer him as a substitute, for the meal just served was the last one of the flight and almost everything had been used up. There was no doubt about it, she thought dismally, bad luck had dogged her almost from the moment of her first meeting with Kent Travers. 'I'm terribly sorry—'

'What else have you?' Kent put down the container and Simoni looked at it, not daring to raise her head.

'Only ch-cheese and b-biscuits, sir.'

An oath issued from his lips. 'Cheese and biscuits! What sort of a meal will that make?'

Simoni spread her hands in a helpless gesture. 'There's nothing else—'

'You do realize we've still a three-hour flight before us?'

'Yes, sir, I do, and I'm most upset about this—'

'And that by the time I do get something I'll have been about eight hours without a proper meal.'

She nodded dumbly. His last meal he had taken before Miles, and that meant it was now almost four hours since he had eaten.

'Won't you have the cheese, sir?' she managed unhappily at last.

A sharp intake of his breath and then,

'Make me a cup of coffee! That's surely something you can do right!'

No sooner had they arrived at the Britt than Simoni left the other crew members and went up to her room. She was tired and dispirited, and more than a little bit afraid something really serious might eventually go wrong.

'I'm sure it will,' she quivered, going into the bathroom to take a shower. 'One of these days something awful will happen – I'm certain of it!'

Later on in the evening Simoni and Dawn, an A.L.M. from another aircraft, went to the Gulf Hotel to dine. As they sat drinking sherries Miles and Geoff appeared and whisked them off to dance.

'You here? I didn't see you come in?' Simoni smiled at Miles as she fell into step with him.

'We've only just arrived – a whole crowd of us from the Britt. The others are still in the bar.'

'You're dining here, though?'

'Yes, we're dining here. I'll get one of the waiters to put the tables together and we can make one big party.'

Simoni moistened her lips. 'Is Captain Travers

here?' she asked, and Miles looked at her in some amusement.

'Of course. The man's ravenous,' he laughed, and received a darkling glance from his partner.

'Miles,' warned Simoni quietly, 'be very careful!'

'Scratch my eyes out, would you?' He laughed again, but then became more serious. 'Not still worrying your pretty head about that gammon, surely?'

'I have the most infernal luck, Miles. He puts the hoodoo on me! Why in heaven's name did I have to get the container that was wrongly marked? I'd bet every penny I possess that it was the *only one* in the whole unit that was wrongly marked.' She paused and added, 'What really troubles me is that something really catastrophic might happen one of these days.'

'Nonsense. How can it?' She made no reply and he went on, 'Stop worrying about that blasted meal. The episode's over and done with now, so you can forget all about it.'

'Till the next time,' she murmured with a fatalistic sigh.

Miles laughed again.

'He doesn't bear malice, that's one thing about the boss. You have to admit that, Simoni.'

'He doesn't—? I don't know where you got that idea. He most certainly does bear malice. Yesterday he even reminded me of the package we brought away from Akrotiri on the last trip here.'

Miles shrugged. 'You take these things to heart, Simoni – attach far too much importance to them.' He led her off the floor, smiled at her and patted her shoulder soothingly. 'I'll get hold of the waiter and see about the tables. Ten minutes from now you'll have ditched your blues and be your usual cheerful self!'

And Miles proved to be right. The company was gay and, apart from Dawn – and of course Simoni herself – all male.

They had a sumptuous meal, Kent Travers ordering a huge steak, she noticed, and finishing off with a sweet, which he normally never ate.

As they were outnumbered by the men, Simoni and Dawn found themselves dancing nearly all the time. Kent danced twice with Dawn and although Simoni did not expect him to dance with her she felt the omission deeply, considering herself slighted. She watched him with Dawn. He was a superb dancer, with a sort of graceful majesty about his every movement. Dawn was looking up at him; she said something and they both laughed. There was no doubt that Kent was an extremely attractive man, and with his own sex he was also very popular.

Miles said something and Simoni turned, joining in the conversation and for the moment forgetting all about Kent Travers.

'I'm just telling Hugh here about your job. He's green with envy.' Hugh was the engineer on the same aircraft as Dawn. He was leaving the Force in eighteen months' time, he told Simoni, and he wondered how he was going to settle down in civilian life after the adventures and travels to which he had become used.

'That's how I was,' admitted Simoni when he had finished speaking. 'I felt I must continue travelling for a while yet, so I hit upon the idea of studying geology. It seemed to offer enormous scope.'

'I might think along those lines myself,' returned

Hugh thoughtfully. 'I suppose it's a bit late now, though.'

'Simoni's been studying for—' Miles stopped, glancing questioningly at her. 'Three years, is it?'

'Just over. I was twenty when I started the course.' She turned, realizing that George was looking over her shoulder. Kent was standing there, while Dawn was now dancing with someone else.

'Shall we dance, Simoni?' The tones were quiet, but they gave her a start. Simoni. . . . Aware of the amused glances of the rest of the crew, she made a swift recovery and, rising from her chair, she moved with Kent towards the dance floor. She did not really want to dance with him, she thought, frowning, and steeled herself to the physical impact. What had come over the captain at this late hour? The evening was drawing to a close – in fact some of their party had already left the hotel and gone back to Britannia House. Perhaps he had suddenly realized it was not good manners to dance with one girl and not with the other. Yes, that was it. Kent would be a stickler for manners and as there were only two girls in the company he would naturally consider it incumbent on him to dance with them both.

Presently Kent said, swinging her away from a laughing couple who threatened to collide with them,

'I gather you've managed to get the type of post you were looking for?'

'I had the interview yesterday.' Simoni felt shy all at once and lacking in confidence. 'I'm expecting a letter.'

'So you're not actually sure?' He looked question-

45

ingly at her. 'From the little I overheard just now I inferred you'd been successful.'

'The man I'll be working for assured me the post was mine, but of course I can't be absolutely certain until I receive confirmation by letter.' The fullness of her voice diminished as she spoke; Kent's interest disconcerted her after the more usual manner of indifference he invariably adopted towards her at times like this when, being off duty, they shared some social event. On all previous occasions she had been treated as a negligible participant in the gathering, Kent plainly considering her to be far outside the range of his attention.

'You'll be working for one particular man?' His eyes looked down; she became more disconcerted by the faintly sardonic expression now lingering in their depths. No doubt in Simoni's mind as to his thoughts. It was to be hoped she would prove more efficient in the future than she had in the past. She could almost have reminded him of the opinion of her former boss, but she refrained.

'Yes, I shall be working with one man, for the most part, that is.'

He still regarded her with that watchful and sardonic look, seeming intent on taking in every detail of her beautifully-moulded features, and she wondered if he were seeing his ex-fiancée. Had he been terribly in love? Somehow she could not picture Kent deeply involved, not emotionwise. He was too cold, too *masculine*, somehow. From her own experience of him Simoni had formed what she believed was a true impression of his character. When a man entered into a relationship with a woman he must lower his guard, must of necessity gear his temperament to the softer, gentler aspect of life, simply because a woman was by nature warm and sensitive, and a romantic. Kent Travers was, as she had always maintained, a man's man; he was hard and tough, and Simoni felt instinctively that he would consider it a weakness on his part were he to soften to a woman's level. Perhaps his job helped to make him what he was, being both dangerous and demanding, calling for courage and stamina, and of course, initiative and the ability to command.

To Simoni's intense surprise she suddenly found herself being propelled gently to the open window.

'It's hot,' was all Kent said by way of explanation for his unexpected conduct, and she glanced swiftly up at him, as well she might, for the air conditioning within the hotel brought down the temperature to a much lower degree than that outside. But she did not see how she could voice any objection to their going out, even had she the desire to do so – which, to her wonderment, she had not. The garden was night-scented, the air balmy and soft; the sparkling waters of the Arabian Gulf floated away to where the star-spangled vault of the sky ended in the line that was the horizon. Palms swayed against the moon, so that everything became streaked with silver and casting the landscape and the trees into ever-shifting light and shade. Simoni darted a glance at her companion, to whose face this play of light and shade brought an almost startlingly harsh effect. Harsh she had never considered him – a disciplinarian, a tyrant in all matters pertaining to his work, but never before had she been aware of the harsh quality which she now perceived.

'Tell me about your job?' The request was spoken

47

more like an order.

'I don't know very much myself, yet,' Simoni frankly admitted, going on to tell him about the interview. 'I shall be working in a laboratory some of the time,' she went on to explain. 'But I shall also be flying.' She smiled at him, turning her head again as she did so. 'I'm very lucky to be able to fly in my job, because I love it.'

He nodded musingly and said, as if to himself,

'Yes, it's great to fly ... the getting up before dawn, the take-off in the grey first light, and then the whole indescribable spread of glory as you fly into the sunrise. The whole world is yours as you soar above the clouds, leaving the rest of mankind to its earth-bound chores.'

He was not with her; she stared at him, stunned by this side to him which had never before been revealed, even in the smallest degree.

Soundless moments of preoccupation followed, while for Simoni the situation became more and more unreal. She felt tensed but dared not break into this mood of abstraction where her presence was forgotten. How strange it was to be like this with Kent Travers, her severe and exacting superior officer, sitting in the gardens of the hotel, drenched in the atmosphere of the East, in the unsurpassed magic and beauty of an Arabian night. It was a time for romance, for stolen kisses and new awakenings ... a time for love. Startled by her wandering fancies, she put an instant brake on them, but despite her efforts at stern self-discipline she could not control her emotions, nor calm the sudden wild pulsation of her heart.

She tried to speak, found nothing to say and sat

48

straight up, her hands clasped in her lap. Why was she here with Kent? What could two people hitherto seldom in harmony find to share in the magic of this tropical night? Her throat was dry and her nerves taut. What was this state of tantalizing emotions elusively defying her efforts at interpretation?

Simoni could neither explain her feelings nor bear them, and she turned hesitantly to Kent and said,

'Hadn't we better be going back to the others?'

'The others?' He glanced at his watch. 'It's time we were heading back to the Britt. I'll get a taxi.'

A taxi for two. . . .

'I came with Dawn,' she reminded him breathlessly, but even as she spoke she heard the gay chatter issuing from the front of the hotel, and seconds later several taxis drove away. 'She's gone. . . .' Simoni's nerves fluttered. Vague yearnings assailed her. She knew an exciting and delicate access of expectancy. Kent neither moved nor spoke and she shot him a timid sidelong glance. 'Dawn's gone. . . .' she repeated.

'Never mind. As I said, I'll get a taxi for us.' He seemed to lean across her as he stood up, and his face came close to hers. She sheered back abruptly, her pulse vibrating in some unfathomable way.

'Come,' he said, and she rose to her feet. But Kent made no further move and neither did she. It was an electric moment, setting her emotions on fire.

This was unbearable, she thought, yet still she was unable to move away from Kent. What was happening to her? – and to him, for that matter? He turned his head and their eyes met. Simoni quivered, caught and torn by the emotions of pleasure and pain, of eager yet indefinable expectancy and a sort of exquisite fear.

From the sea a faint breeze had risen to sway the palms; it picked up exotic perfumes and carried them to their nostrils while its warmth caressed their faces, gently. Kent's reaching for Simoni's hand should have been regarded by her as an unexpected gesture, but it was not. It was part of this magic, this interlude of unreality where she and Kent were in complete harmony. Yet she whispered, 'This is crazy' even as she allowed herself to be drawn unresistingly into his arms. His lips found hers, hard and demanding; Simoni responded, driven by some madness completely alien to her nature. She was transfixed, pliant in his embrace, trapped by the power of him and his intense masculine attraction. Her surrendering lips fanned his ardour and she was caught by the whirlwind of his passion, pressed close to his body, overpowered because of his height and his strength and her own inability to resist. It was a long while before he held her away from him, and the smiling grey eyes lacked their customary hard light just as his tones had lost their crisp and cutting sting.

'Simoni ... you're very beautiful,' he murmured. 'But then I've always known. . . .' His voice trailed away into silence, but not before Simoni had caught and understood the curious emphasis it contained.

He had kissed her because she resembled his fianceé!

Burning all over now, but for a totally different reason, Simoni twisted from his embrace and started to run towards the hotel entrance. He soon caught her up, asking what was wrong.

'I hate you!' she quivered. 'I hated you before, but it was nothing to this! Oh, how dare you kiss me – how dare you!'

He stared, taken aback by this unexpected demonstration.

'What the devil's got into you?' he demanded, recovering instantly.

'You're detestable!' Still shaken more by her stimulated emotions than her anger, she raked him scornfully from head to foot. 'Whatever my opinion of you I at least believed you to be a gentleman!' Her voice vibrated, echoing the disturbance within her. It was only when Kent threw back his head and laughed that she realized just how ridiculous was her furious outburst.

'You're absurd! You wanted me to kiss you— No, don't you dare deny it, Simoni. You can't with truth – not the way you've just behaved, offering neither protest nor resistance. I gave you plenty of warning and had you made even the hint of a stand I'd have desisted, naturally.' His voice was edged with mockery, his glance gave evidence of the amusement he felt. Tears of mortification stood on Simoni's lashes; she blinked, but they fell on to her cheeks and she averted her head, as she had on so many other occasions when confronted with this man, but this time it was to hide more than her discomfiture at his scathing injunctions. It was to hide her own shame, to keep from him the expression of self-disgust she knew would be revealed in her eyes.

'Are you going to call the taxi?' Her tones were low and stilted; she wondered how she and Kent would revert to the old relationship and wished with all her heart she had not come to the Gulf Hotel tonight. She hadn't been at all keen, she recalled, but she had allowed Dawn to persuade her.

Re-entering the hotel, Simoni stood aside while Kent gave orders for a taxi to come for them. They drove in silence along Palace Road and then along the Causeway, built up on the coral foundation to link the islands of Bahrain and Muharraq, where Britannia House was situated.

The silence was broken a short while before they reached their destination.

'Why so withdrawn, Simoni? You're not still in a temper, surely?'

She looked ahead, at the lights along the dual carriageway linking the two islands.

'No, I'm not still in a temper.'

'Silly, wasn't it?' Mockery now in his voice and Simoni bit her lips to keep them from trembling. 'Women are such odd creatures,' he went on, his humour expressed by the dryness of his tone. 'They ask for attention and then adopt this air of injury, of indignation.' He produced an easy smile. 'They all conform to a pattern – are so transparently predictable.'

She retorted, driven by humiliation, 'They're also honest, Captain!'

'Meaning I am not?' He turned his head sharply. 'I must ask you to explain that.' The voice of her superior, rapping forth an order. Simoni answered quietly,

'It isn't honest to pretend.' The words were out before she realized they could be misunderstood and she knew no surprise when he said,

'Any pretence was on your part—'

'Mine?' diverted. 'In what way did I pretend?'

He uttered an impatient sigh. 'We both did what we did for the enjoyment of the moment. I freely admit that, but you don't, apparently. This belated protest, for example, what sense is there in it? – this condemnation of me as a sort of cad who took advantage of you. As I've already said, you're ridiculous.'

Stung, and hurt in a way she could not understand, Simoni returned,

'You're in the habit of kissing girls for the enjoyment of the moment?'

He laughed at that. 'Have you ever met a man who isn't?'

The colour flooded her cheeks, and for a while she remained silent. But then she said,

'When I spoke of honesty just now, and pretence, I didn't mean what you thought I meant.'

'No?' inquiringly.

She swallowed, playing for a little time because her words were difficult to voice.

'You kissed me, Captain Travers, because I resembled the girl to whom you were once engaged.'

A profound silence filled the car; she felt Kent stiffen on the seat beside her, heard the swift intake of his breath. Had she touched him on a raw spot? Simoni hoped she had. Despite this rather vindictive wish, however, she knew a hint of trepidation. She should not have said that. After all, Kent Travers was her superior and he would not suffer any infringement of the boundary separating them. But to her surprise he said, although in tones set to freeze her very marrow,

'How, may I ask, do you happen to know what my ex-fiancée looked like?'

Simoni plucked at a button on her dress.

'Someone in the Mess remarked on my likeness to her.' The taxi stopped and the driver opened the door.

Simoni stepped out followed by Kent. The driver received his money and went off, leaving them standing there, in the shadows, for it was very late and most of the lights in Britannia House had been extinguished.

'I see.' Kent spoke at last, an edge to his voice. He was far from pleased at learning that he had been the object of discussion in the Sergeants' Mess. He looked down at her from an incredible height, but said no more until they were inside and then, in the cool impersonal tone he might have used had they both been on duty, 'Good night, Sergeant.'

Simoni swallowed something hurtful in her throat; and because her face burned she kept it from his gaze.

'Good night, Captain,' she said, and turning from him she ran up the stairs. As she closed her bedroom door she heard the light spring of his steps, taking two stairs at a time. And then he was passing her door, whistling softly to himself.

The incident and subsequent interchange remained with Simoni long after she was in bed, and all the while she throbbed with the consciousness of her own shame. She knew what had happened. The unreality of the situation where Kent Travers was no longer the impersonal being who was her boss, the moon and the sea, the magic of an Eastern night . . . all this and a man as undeniably attractive as Captain Kent Travers. . . .

What must he think of her? On the surface he had been amused and faintly mocking – but underneath he could only feel contempt for her, regarding her reciprocation as the sort of abandon so much in evidence in these permissive times. She was no better and no worse than the rest. Perhaps he was convinced he could have taken her had he chosen to do so.

'I can't ever face him again,' was her last thought before she finally dropped into a troubled sleep. But of course she did face him, for she must work with him for another five months.

CHAPTER FOUR

DESPITE Simoni's fears, nothing catastrophic occurred during her last five months of service, and in fact, these months were comparatively uneventful where her work was concerned. Kent was ever brusque and impersonal and the incident at the Gulf Hotel might never have taken place.

He said good-bye to her two days before she was due to leave, for he and his crew were flying to the Middle East and would not be returning for about a week. He and Simoni were alone in the crew room and he extended a hand to her, his manner cool and disinterested.

'Good luck in your new job,' he said as Simoni gave him her hand.

'Thank you, sir.' She glanced up, pale and small beside him. 'I wish you good luck, too, in your new work.' Kent had only two more weeks to go and then he also would be leaving.

'Thank you.' A little silence followed; Simoni was surprised by the impression that Kent was lost for words. But after a while he said, 'You seem bent on a career – aren't you interested in marriage? I thought you had a boy-friend.'

She looked down at her hands, silent for a space, recalling that kiss and her own shameful lack of control. Strange it was, and quite unfair, that a man could drive off in a spate of ardour, but a woman must practise reserve. Not that Simoni was in the habit of losing control – the incident in the hotel gardens was her first real awakening, and even though she was swept away by the romance of the atmosphere and by Kent's magnificence, she knew for sure that at the crucial moment she would have resisted him. But in his ignorance of this, Kent's manner towards her since that night had ever been one of faint contempt.

'My friendship with Matthew is purely platonic. We're not intending to marry.'

Kent looked down at her, quirking an eyebrow. Did he believe her to be 'easy'? she wondered with an unhappy little sigh. All he said was, 'Well, you know best what you want. Good-bye, and again – good luck.'

Three months later Simoni was visiting her parents at their home near Brighton. They had been shopping and Simoni was unpacking the baskets and putting the provisions away in the fridge. Her mother was at the sink, preparing a salad for their tea.

'I wish you'd come home, dear,' she said, not for the first time. 'I've three children and they're all roamers. I never see any of you for any length of time.'

Simoni smiled, reminding her mother that she had been the one to say,

'Travel, all of you. You're not fully educated until you've travelled.'

'Yes, I did say that,' Mrs. Clarke admitted. 'But I didn't mean you to go on travelling for ever! Cindy's in Canada – though why she should go there to be a nanny I really don't know. There are plenty of jobs here. Then Stephen's hitch-hiking around Europe somewhere – I never know where he is half the time.' Mrs. Clarke put the lettuce in a clean tea towel and

57

shook it over the sink. 'What about this young man you had in the Air Force? Aren't you going to marry him?'

'I'm not marrying anyone for a long while yet, Mother. I'm happy in my new job and if I stay with the firm I'll do very well for myself in a few years' time.'

'A few years! You're going to be too old for marriage!'

Simoni laughed, saying it would be a long while before she was too old for marriage.

'I don't know if I want to be tied to a house all day,' she added, but although her voice was light her thoughts were somewhat painful. For stupid as she knew it to be she often found herself thinking of Kent Travers, and that incident at Bahrain. But it was not then that she had begun to care – Simoni knew that now. Kent Travers had loomed far too large in her thoughts right from the start. And since that last good-bye it had been more difficult than ever to cast his image away, for it seemed that the harder she tried the more it persistently intruded into her mental vision. He was not for her, she admitted that and, therefore, she must forget him. Her job was interesting and exacting and all her hopes of forgetting her formidable ex-boss were centred on it.

'Marriage doesn't mean that these days.' Her mother's faintly indignant voice broke into her musings and Simoni turned, closing the door of the fridge.

'Perhaps not,' she agreed, but added, 'Marriage is tying, for all that, and I'm not yet ready to be tied.'

Her mother shrugged. 'Things are so different now.

When I was young we were all terrified of being left on the shelf.'

'So you rushed into marriage on account of it.'

'I wouldn't say that. I didn't take the first one who came along.'

'I'm jolly glad you didn't, otherwise I shouldn't have such a wonderful dad—'

'Someone taking my name in vain.' Mr. Clarke came in from the garden and smiled affectionately at his daughter. 'I'm glad you appreciate how lucky you are!'

Simoni laughed, but his wife threw him a deprecating glance.

'It's a good thing, Dave, that you don't wear a hat!'

'Take no notice of her,' advised Simoni. 'Mother doesn't mean half she says.'

'I meant every word of what I was saying just now. Dad, don't you think it's high time Simoni began thinking of settling down?'

'Well . . . it would be nice to have a few little nippers calling me Grandpa.'

'Cindy might oblige – or Stephen, when he's older, of course.' Stephen was only nineteen and his girl-friends were so numerous that none of the family could keep track of them.

'You're the eldest,' Dad reminded her. 'As Mother says, you should be thinking of settling down.' He took a seat in the little breakfast area of the kitchen and brought out his pipe. 'What about this Bill? He seems a nice young fellow – and he likes you, Simoni, no doubt of that. When's he coming, by the way?'

'Tomorrow. He'll stay for the week-end and then

we'll travel back to London together on Sunday night.'

'He likes coming here, doesn't he? Said he enjoyed it no end last time.'

'I'm glad you invited him,' intervened Mrs. Clarke. 'I agree with Dad, he's a nice young man.' She looked round and Simoni handed her a salad bowl. 'Have you set the table, dear?'

'Yes. I'll cut the bread now.'

'Tell me about this projected trip?' Simoni's father urged a short while later as they were having their meal. 'It's an aerial survey, you said, to the desert again, I gather?'

Simoni nodded, but her mother spoke before she could do so.

'In one of those tiny planes?'

'Of course.'

Mrs. Clarke shook her head. 'I don't like it, Simoni. They never seem safe to me – not like the big ones.'

'They're perfectly safe,' laughed Simoni. 'All aircraft have to be airworthy, otherwise they wouldn't be in use.'

'I think you're very brave. You'd never get me in one like that. How many passengers do they hold?'

'Five – at least this one does.'

'You've seen it?'

'No, but I've met the pilot and he told me all about it.'

'And another thing,' went on Mrs. Clarke a trifle broodingly, 'those Arabs. They're not like us, you know. They have harems—'

'What on earth has that to do with it!' exclaimed her

husband. 'Simoni's not thinking of marrying an Arab!'

'The Arabs I've met are very good people,' put in Simoni gently. 'They're warm-hearted and generous, and extremely friendly.'

'In the towns, maybe. But what about those Bedouins?'

Simoni's eyes lit with amusement. 'What about them?'

'With a job like yours you could be stranded in the desert—'

'Now why should I be stranded in the desert?'

'People have been, many a time.'

Simoni shrugged. 'I don't think you need worry your head about that, darling. I shan't be stranded in the desert, I assure you.'

Bill arrived before lunch time the following day and was warmly welcomed by Simoni's parents.

'Show him to his room, dear.' Mrs. Clarke looked at Simoni. 'I've put him in the one facing the orchard this time.'

'I'll get my bag from the car.' Bill smiled at Simoni and went out. She met him in the hall as he returned with the suitcase. 'It's great to be here, Simoni. I think your people are wonderful to ask me.'

'Mum and Dad love having visitors. Besides,' she added mischievously, 'they look upon you as a potential husband for me.' They reached the top of the stairs and as Simoni led the way into the bedroom Bill remarked,

'You didn't tell them what I said?'

'Said?' She went over to the window and opened it, then turned to face him.

'I said, if you remember, "How is it that I can neither persuade you to marry me nor get you to have an affair with me?"'

Simoni laughed, pulling out a drawer to make sure it was empty.

'They'd be horrified at that latter suggestion, and instantly show you the door.'

'All right,' resignedly, putting his case on a chair. 'I can wait.'

'All these drawers are empty,' she said. 'And the wardrobe. I'll leave you to sort yourself out.' She was at the door when he said,

'The coming trip – it isn't being taken in the company's aircraft. We've chartered a craft from a private company.'

She swung round, a nerve fluttering. 'A – a private company?'

'Yes, and what do you think? I know the boss! Isn't that a coincidence? Went to school with him. He was in the Air Force until recently. . . .' Bill's voice faded. 'Are you all right, Simoni? You've gone awfully pale.'

'This man . . . what's his name?' Why ask? Simoni knew his name.

'Kent Travers. He's a great guy. You'll like him no end.'

She swallowed hard and then,

'I'll like him, you say? Why, shall I be meeting him personally? He isn't piloting our aircraft, surely?'

'No, of course not. But we have to pick up the aircraft at Nicosia, so he's asked us to stay the night with him at his home.'

'Us?'

'All of us, naturally – you, me and the photographer.'

'Did – did you tell him my name?'

Bill frowned in puzzlement. 'No, why should I? He knows we're two men and a woman, of course.' He paused a moment. 'Is anything wrong, Simoni?'

Absently she fingered the knob of the door. To see Kent again when she was trying so hard to forget him, to be a guest in his house knowing full well he would never have extended the invitation had he known she was included in it.

'Not really,' she answered at last, realizing Bill was standing there, above his open suitcase, waiting in some perplexity for her to speak. 'But – but Kent Travers was my captain during my last year of service.'

'He was? Then why the dismal look? You'll have lots to talk about.'

A faintly bitter smile hovered about her mouth.

'We were far from friendly, Bill. In fact, we didn't get on right from the word go.'

His frown returned. 'I can't imagine anyone not getting on with Kent, nor can I imagine anyone not getting on with you. How very strange,' he added thoughtfully.

'I believe I closely resemble the girl he was engaged to. She played him a dirty trick and at first it was probably a shock to be confronted by me. Afterwards he was cool and impersonal, that's all,' she hastily added on seeing Bill's expression change. 'He wasn't hostile, don't let me give that impression. But later everything I did went wrong and a – well, I suppose you would call it a sort of animosity that sprang up between us. Ours was never the friendly, comradely relationship that exists in the Force among crews – especially when they're off duty. With my other captain we had a very

63

nice social life and I, like everyone else, was allowed to use his nickname. It was not so with Captain Travers. I never ever felt free to relax with him. . . .' Her voice fell to a whisper before fading into silence. Only once had she and Kent relaxed with one another. . . .

They flew to Nicosia and were met by Kent himself. He and Simoni stared at one another for several seconds, Kent with only faint surprise, while Simoni's silence resulted from lack of confidence. Had this been Captain Holmes she would have greeted him enthusiastically, responding to his pleasure at seeing her. Not so with Kent.

'So we meet again, Simoni?' He held out a hand and she took it. 'You know, when I fell to thinking about this little party whom I'd invited to my house I did wonder if the female member could be you.'

'Did you?' Her mouth felt dry and she coughed. It was a nervous action which brought a faint smile to his lips. He understood how she felt, evidently. 'I expect the idea *would* occur to you.'

'I was so amazed when Simoni told me you two had worked together.' Bill spoke after watching the meeting with keen interest. 'You'll have some reminiscing to do,' he added in spite of what Simoni had told him. He turned to Martin, the photographer, and introduced him to Kent.

'Pleased to meet you.' Martin was middle-aged and somehow Simoni had gained the impression he was not strong. His lips would go blue sometimes and he would seem to have difficulty with his breathing. 'It's most kind of you to have us spend the night in your home.'

'It's a pleasure.'

Was it by accident that his eyes avoided hers as he said that? wondered Simoni. Perhaps not. She mustn't begin by being fanciful about the invitation. The visit would have its awkward moments without her deliberately creating more by allowing her imagination to run free.

Kent drove them through the Turkish sector, then through the wooded mountain pass cutting the Kyrenia Range before they dropped into the lovely town of Kyrenia, on the northern side of the island. On reaching the edge of the town he turned right and after travelling a few miles they came to the village of Ayios Epiktitos where, high on the hillside, stood a Cypriot-style house, white and modern, with shaded verandahs and patios and a magnificent view down to the still aquamarine waters of the Mediterranean. One end of the house was on stilts; Kent drove the car under this and they all got out. It was early May and remnants of the glorious spring remained, with colour still ablaze on the hillsides and in the fields – the brilliant yellow of the crown daisies and the scarlet of the poppies. There were the purple scrambling bindweed and the dainty upright sword lily.

'I expect you've been to Cyprus before?' Kent's glance by-passed both Simoni and Bill and rested on Martin, who instantly nodded. 'So none of us are strangers to the island.' He walked with Martin as they all strolled towards the steps leading up to the main part of the house. From the sitting-room the view was breathtaking. Directly below the golden beach was the narrow winding road leading to the village, its borders gleaming with wild flowers while the drop on the far side was clothed with trees – the carobs with their long sweet pods still green, the lemons, and some orange trees too, their bright shiny leaves contrasting with the rather dull silver-grey foliage of the olive trees. Below these slopes was the golden beach, drenched in sunshine. It was one of the most popular beaches on the northern coast, but, at this time of the year, it was deserted, for Cypriots, used as they are to the heat, never bathed until late June or July. Simoni, however, decided to ask to be excused later and take a swim, for the water would be sufficiently warm for her.

'This is a very lovely house,' Bill remarked, looking out from the wide window to the spreading panorama below. 'You bought it, you said? I always thought it was impossible to buy a house in Cyprus. I understood one had to build.'

'Normally one builds, because as you say houses are seldom for sale. However, I was fortunate with this because the people who built it for their retirement decided they didn't want to settle here after all. It isn't exactly as I want it, but I shall have the alterations done very shortly.'

'It's convenient for Nicosia, too. You were lucky, Kent, very lucky indeed.'

Kent turned his head as a young Cypriot girl entered the room in response to his summons from the bell.

'Julia, will you show Miss Clarke up to the room you've prepared for her?'

'Yes, Mr. Kent.' Julia looked Simoni up and down, then smiled at her. 'Have you a bag, miss?'

'All the bags are in the boot of the car,' Kent informed her. 'Get Michael to bring them in.'

'Yes, Mr. Kent.'

'When you've taken Miss Clarke up you can then show our gentlemen visitors to their rooms.'

'Yes, Mr. Kent.'

It was only midday and an hour later lunch was served. Afterwards, when they had coffee served to them on the patio, Bill hitched his chair close to Simoni's so that he could slip an arm along the back of her chair. The action went unnoticed by Simoni, because they were all conversing. But suddenly her eyes were drawn to Kent's and she frowned in perplexity at the contempt she noticed there. Then as Bill's hand dropped on to her shoulder she understood. By rights she should have given Kent stare for stare, conveying her indifference to his opinion, whatever it might be. But Simoni blushed instead, hiding her embarrassment behind lowered lashes. After a long while she glanced up; Kent was talking to Martin, but his eyes flickered to her for a moment. Their expression was now one of cool indifference. Simoni rose from her chair, saying, with a forced smile that embraced them all,

'Do you mind my leaving you? I'm going for a swim.'

'Swim? – in May?' Bill frowned at her.

'We're in Cyprus.'

'I don't care; the water's not warm enough yet.'

'Not for you, perhaps, but it is for me.'

'How do you know?'

'From past experience, of course.' She looked at Kent, asking again if he minded.

'Why should I?' he asked, disconcerting her.

'I'm a guest in your house. It would scarcely be good manners just to go off without asking if you minded.' Not that he would mind, she knew that. On the contrary, he would be glad, because then they could all indulge in men's talk.

'No, Simoni, I don't mind at all, but you do realize the beach is not quite so close as it appears from here?'

She glanced down. 'Isn't there a direct path?'

'No, one has to use the road, and as it winds about the distance is about three-quarters of a mile.'

'That's not far to walk. What time's tea?' she then asked. 'I wouldn't care to be late.'

'I usually have tea about four-thirty to five. We'll dine at eight-thirty.' Kent stopped and his eyes strayed to the end of the patio. Julia was beckoning him.

'The telephone, Mr. Kent,' she said urgently.

'Excuse me.' He rose and went into the house.

The three chatted and Simoni was still there when Kent returned, his face pale and his mouth set tight. Simoni knew there was something seriously wrong even before he spoke.

'I'm very sorry, Martin, but the trip can't take place tomorrow as planned.'

'Not—?' Martin looked at him. 'I don't understand?'

'My secretary's just rung to tell me your pilot's had an accident in his car and he's in hospital.'

'So we haven't a pilot?'

'I can take you myself, but not tomorrow. In fact,' he added, 'I can't say just when I shall be able to take you.' He paused a moment, and then with sudden decision he went on to explain that Ian, the pilot, was a great friend of his. That morning his wife had left him – gone off with another man – and that, in Kent's opinion, was the indirect cause of the accident, because normally Ian was the safest of drivers.

'From what little my secretary knows Ian drove into a tree on the side of the road. Obviously his mind was affected by this action of his wife's—' Abruptly Kent broke off. Watching him closely, Simoni was fascinated by the quickening of a muscle at the side of his throat. The cool imperturbable Kent Travers was, astoundingly, under the influence of some severe emotional strain. 'There are two children,' Kent continued presently. 'I've decided to have them until Ian comes out of hospital and can arrange for someone to take care of them.'

'The children are coming here?'

'My secretary, Miss Benson, is bringing them shortly, as they're alone in the house. Meanwhile, I'm going to the hospital to see Ian.' He was still rather pale beneath the tan; his eyes were narrowed and it was not difficult to guess that he was thinking of the children's mother, and wholeheartedly condemning her action in leaving her family.

'What some women will do,' Martin was saying in tones of disgust. 'It's difficult to believe.'

'Not with this woman!' Kent spoke with such hate and vehemence that Simoni stared at him in amazement. He couldn't have displayed more fury had he personally been involved. 'It surprises me that she's stayed with Ian as long as she has.' He made a gesture with his hands then, a gesture of apology. 'I must go, but I expect to be back before dinner. Make yourselves at home. Later we'll arrange about your flight. I can take you myself, as I said, but I must get this matter settled first. Ring your company on my telephone, Bill, and see if they'd prefer you to charter another plane or whether they're willing to put off the trip for a day or two.'

'Thanks, Kent, I'll do that.' Then Bill added, 'I rather think there'd be difficulty in chartering a plane at such short notice, so I'm fairly certain they'll decide to await your convenience. Shall we arrange to stay at an hotel? We can't inflict ourselves on you at a time like this—'

'You must certainly stay here, all of you. I won't hear of your staying at an hotel.'

From her bedroom window Simoni watched the car drive from the grounds and she followed it with her eyes as it wound down the narrow stony road towards Kyrenia.

Simoni went for her swim, but she felt restless and soon returned to the house.

'You haven't been long?' Bill and Martin were still on the patio; they had been reading, but glanced up as she approached them.

'It isn't the right atmosphere for relaxing,' she answered with a grimace. 'One is struck with the drama of this situation in which Kent's involved.'

'It is disconcerting,' agreed Bill, bringing a chair forward for her.

'I'll not sit down yet, Bill. I must take a shower and then get dressed. Those little children will be here soon, or so I should imagine.'

When Simoni came back to the patio the two men were just going for a stroll. Soon after their departure Simoni heard a car pull up and she looked out across the garden to where a tall, elegantly-dressed girl was just emerging from the driver's seat. Opening the rear door, she said something and the two little girls slid out,

70

with much less confidence, and stood looking around them, a frightened expression on their faces.

'Come on!' The voice was sharp and a small frown creased Simoni's brow. 'What are you looking at? Come on, I said!'

The children followed reluctantly, giving a little skip each time the woman glanced back, her manner one of impatience. She approached the steps unerringly; obviously used to the house, decided Simoni, leaning back in her chair as the woman and her two charges disappeared from view.

Moments later Simoni heard the conversation going on between the woman and Julia.

'Ah, you've brought the little ones, Miss Thora. Mr. Kent said to expect you, and he said I was to take care of them until he gets back.'

'I know all this,' shortly. 'Mr. Kent spoke to me on the telephone, remember.'

'Yes, Miss Thora,' came the meek response.

'Catherine – Vicki, do come along! You'll stay with Julia until Uncle Kent comes home—'

'I want my daddy,' began one of the children in a fretful tone.

'Don't be a baby! – good gracious, are you crying, at your age?'

'She's only five,' cut in the other child indignantly. 'She's crying because Mummy's gone and Daddy's in hospital. We don't like being here.'

'There, there,' came the soothing tones of Julia. 'I'll take good care of you till your uncle gets back. He's gone to see your daddy, and he'll tell you all about it when he comes back. Come, little girl, let me dry your eyes.'

'Julia, for heaven's sake stop pandering to the silly child! Catherine, look to your sister. It seems to me that a good smack wouldn't do any harm!'

Rising anger brought the colour flooding to Simoni's cheeks. What a heartless woman! And how could she have so little understanding of children? Unable to listen a moment longer, Simoni entered the house and made for the hall. Julia looked up and smiled, obviously relieved to see her.

Thora turned, and stared uncomprehendingly.

'Who are you?' she demanded, insolently looking Simoni over from head to foot.

Simoni's fists clenched, but she managed to speak in a calm and level tone as she made her reply.

'I'm a guest here. Is there anything I can do?'

'A guest?' frowned Thora, ignoring the question. 'Kent said he was entertaining some people who had chartered one of his planes. Are you one of the party?'

'There are two men and myself.' Simoni looked at the two little girls, one with damp lashes and cheeks, the other a little flushed because of her indignation. She had her arm around her sister's shoulders and she was murmuring soothingly to her. Simoni smiled faintly. Even the elder child was a mere babe. 'I asked if there was anything I could do.'

Opening her mouth to make some scathing retort, the girl thought better of it, remembering in time that Simoni was a guest of her employer.

'I don't think Julia requires any help, thank you, Miss – er . . .?'

'Clarke – Simoni Clarke.'

'Well, thanks for your offer, Miss Clarke, but there's

no need for you to put yourself out, or become involved in this ridic— In this unfortunate situation. Julia, you have the children's bedroom ready?'

'Yes, Miss Thora. Mr. Kent said I must do this.'

'Good.' The girl's blue eyes were still on Simoni, cold and carrying an unmistakable shade of animosity. No love lost here, decided Simoni, feeling Thora Benson was just about the least attractive woman she had ever met. Not physically, though, for the girl had all it takes to spell perfection – the slim sylph-like figure and long elegant legs, the peaches and cream skin and deep blue eyes. Her fair hair was long and straight, held back at one side with a mother-of-pearl clip and dropping over her face at the other. Good-looking, no doubt of that – but what a nasty piece of work lay beneath the veneer! Simoni had to smile at her own mental description of the woman's character. Noticing the smile, Thora said in tones sharp to the point of hostility,

'Might I inquire the reason for your amusement, Miss Clarke?'

'I merely smiled at my thoughts, Miss Benson.'

The other girl went red. Turning to Julia, she snapped,

'I'll leave now. See to the children and watch they don't run off.'

'Yes, Miss Thora.'

Thora turned away, making for the front door.

'Aren't you having some refreshment before you go?' Simoni spoke mechanically. It was mid-afternoon and the sun was hot. People never went long without a drink in a climate like this. The girl swung round, her face flaming.

'Miss Clarke,' she said in withering tones, 'I'm

sufficiently at home here to be able to order refreshments, should I desire to do so!'

Simoni swallowed, wondering at the strangeness of her reaction. Could it possibly be that a shaft of jealousy had pierced her? She shrugged away the idea. What had this girl's relationship with Kent to do with her anyway?

CHAPTER FIVE

THE moment Thora left both children started to cry. Taking hold of their hands, Simoni led them out to the patio and, putting two chairs close together, she sat them down, telling Julia to bring three glasses of lemonade and some ice-cream from the fridge.

'I d-don't w-want anything to dr-drink,' sobbed Vicki, clinging to her sister. 'I want my daddy.'

Simoni picked her up, soothing away what little resistance she made, and sat her on her knee.

'Uncle Kent has gone to see Daddy – you know that, don't you?'

'Yes, we do know,' put in Catherine, knuckling her eyes. 'But we want to go to him as well. He's poorly, you see.' Catherine's big brown eyes looked appealingly at Simoni; obviously the child regarded her as a friend. 'Will you take Vicki and me to Daddy?'

'That isn't possible, Catherine – I'm sorry, dear. But perhaps you'll be able to go to the hospital very soon, when Daddy begins to feel a little better.'

Vicki had stopped crying and Simoni dried her eyes, smiling at her and saying in low and gentle tones, 'Daddy wouldn't want you to be unhappy, Vicki, now would he? Come, are you going to let me see you smile?'

'It's because of Mummy as well,' put in Catherine before Vicki could produce the smile. 'She's gone away and Daddy doesn't know where to find her. Do you know where she's gone?'

Simoni swallowed something tight and hard in her throat.

'No, dear, I don't, but she'll be coming back shortly—'

'She won't! Daddy went to look for her and he didn't find her. She's lost—' Catherine began to cry again and Vicki did likewise, in sympathy.

'Come, darlings, you mustn't. . . .' Reaching out, Simoni drew Catherine to her and after a little while her soothing words and gentle embrace had their effect and the children became more controlled. 'There, that's better. You'll have to be smiling when Uncle Kent comes back, won't you?' Catherine nodded and allowed herself to be helped up on to the chair as Julia brought out the drinks and ice-cream on a tray.

'Uncle Kent's nice. He plays with us and buys us presents.'

'He does?' Simoni's eyes flickered strangely. 'Tell me about him.'

'He's big and he laughs and throws you up in the air and catches you,' supplied Vicki, still on Simoni's knee, her head resting against her breast. 'Ooh . . . it's lovely when he throws you up!'

'It's lovely when he catches you as well.' Catherine licked her ice-cream, then made a few stripes on it with the corner of her wafer. 'You think you're going to fall, but you don't!' She glanced across at Simoni, and her eyes had lost their haunted look. 'He bought me this locket—' Catherine tugged at the gold chain and the locket appeared from under her dress. 'It's got Mummy's picture in it. Do you want to see?'

'Yes, please. May I open it?'

'I'll do it for you, because you have to know about

the catch. There – that's Mummy. Isn't she beautiful?' The child leant forward, holding forth the pretty gold locket. Automatically Simoni took it, starting, fascinated at the tiny picture set in the heart-shaped locket. It was incredible, the likeness. ... Simoni swallowed convulsively. This woman, the mother of these two lovely children, had once been engaged to Kent. ... Simoni looked at the children in turn. Neither resembled their mother.

'Do you think she's pretty?' Catherine took back the locket, turning it round so that it was the right way up for her to look on her mother's face. 'Her name's Catherine, just like mine.' The child put away the locket and turned, giving her attention to her ice-cream. 'Do you think she's pretty?' she repeated, digging in her spoon.

'Very pretty.' Before Simoni's vision flitted the picture of Kent on coming from the telephone to impart his news. His harshness was frightening to see. Simoni had thought he might almost have been personally involved. ...

She frowned. It was incomprehensible that Kent should be so friendly with the man who had stolen his fiancée. No, not just friendly with Ian, it seemed, but with his wife, too. Otherwise how was he so well-known to the children? He played with them and gave them presents, so he must be in the habit of visiting them.

Simoni's frown deepened as, trying to unravel the situation, she found herself becoming more and more confused. If Kent had been so friendly with Catherine, then why did he so dislike Simoni, just because she happened to resemble her?

'Vicki,' she said, diverted for a moment, 'aren't you

going to eat your ice-cream?'

'Yes, I think I'll have it now.'

'Do you want to sit on a chair?'

'No, I want to sit here on your knee.' Vicki wriggled closer to the table as Simoni drew the dish of ice-cream towards her. 'Why don't you eat yours?'

'I'm going to.' Simoni picked up her spoon.

'Can I drop some of it in my lemonade?' Catherine looked up a little doubtfully.

'If you wish – yes, of course you can.'

'Ooh, good! It's like a milk shake then!'

'Are you putting it in your lemonade?' Vicki wanted to know, and Simoni shook her head.

'Why? – don't you like it in your lemonade?'

'Not today, Catherine.' She paused and then, 'Have you always lived in Cyprus?'

Catherine shook her head. 'We've only been here a little while. Daddy came because he wanted to fly an aeroplane for Uncle Kent. We lived in Yorkshire before that – near the seaside.' Catherine turned her head. 'Who's that?' she asked as Bill came across from the orchard.

'A friend of Uncle Kent's. He's staying here, just for tonight.'

'Hello there!' Bill ruffled Catherine's head as he passed her. 'And what's your name?' Catherine told him, examined his face for a moment and then, 'Are you this lady's husband?'

'No, little one, but I wish I was.'

'Don't start that just now,' laughed Simoni. 'I have more important things to do than listen to your amorous advances.'

He stared at her.

78

'Advances? My dear Simoni, I've done nothing but retreat since the moment I set eyes on you! The day I take one single step forward I'll put the flag out!'

'Where's Martin?' she wanted to know, changing the subject.

'Coming. He met a man with a donkey and stopped to talk. Martin's like that – enjoys his little chats here and there.'

'He's nice. He should be married, though. He needs looking after.'

'You've not got designs on him, I hope. He's old enough to be your grandfather.'

'My father, Bill. Don't be catty.'

'That's a shemale expression – doesn't apply to males; they're never feline.'

'Lupine, then,' was the swift return, and he glared at her.

'Wretch!'

'Are you having a quarrel?' interrupted Catherine, looking rather alarmed.

'No, dear, why should you think that?'

'My mummy and daddy say horrid things to each other first, just like you did—' Her glance included them both. 'And then they begin to shout and after that they have a big quarrel.'

Bill and Simoni glanced up; their eyes met.

'Sad, very sad.' Bill gave a deep sigh. 'You know, the amazing thing is that all couples start off in love – madly in love. What goes wrong? Can you tell me?'

Simoni shook her head. 'Marriage is frightening,' she murmured, almost to herself. 'As you say, all couples start off in love.' She became pensive. 'Perhaps they don't try,' she added at last, though lamely.

'Why should they have to try? If they're in love it should go smoothly all the while.'

'They don't stay in love, as you've just intimated.'

'What are you talking about?' Vicki leant away and Simoni smiled as she drew out a handkerchief.

'You've put more ice-cream on your nose than in your mouth!'

'I haven't,' Vicki laughed at her. 'It's only a bit.'

'Well, it looks very funny on the end of your nose.'

'She's only young,' submitted Catherine. 'I'm six, but she's only five.'

'I'm more than five!'

'You were five two weeks ago. I remember because we met Uncle Kent in Nicosia and he bought you a doll.'

'I've finished.' Vicki pushed her dish away and leant against Simoni again.

'Quite a pretty little domestic scene.' Bill's voice held banter not unmingled with a hint of pique. Simoni frowned at him. Fortunately, she thought, he did not go on too much. Had he done so her position could have become difficult. She enjoyed her work; it was her whole life and she desired it to continue that way.

The children were still up when Kent returned from the hospital. Simoni was with them on the patio, Bill and Martin being in their rooms, changing for dinner. Simoni had changed a short while earlier and was in a cotton dress, very thin but full and flowing, with a tight-fitting bodice, the neckline low-cut yet not too revealing. Both children left Simoni and ran to Kent, hugging his legs before, with one sweeping move, he had them both aloft in his arms. This was a side of him unsuspected until the information she had received from the children earlier, and she continued to stare. He smiled faintly at her before giving all his attention to the children.

'You've seen Daddy? Is he better?' Catherine spoke through her laughter, her cheek against Kent's. 'Is he coming home soon?'

'In a little while, Catherine,' was the cautious reply. 'You see, he's not quite better and you wouldn't want him to come home until he is, would you?'

Catherine shook her dark head vigorously.

'What did he say about us?' asked Vicki, her hand wound tightly around Kent's neck.

'He sends you both his love and says for you to be very good for Julia.'

'We'll be good.' A small pause and then, from Catherine,

'Can't we have that nice lady to look after us, Uncle Kent?'

He glanced across at Simoni. She was preoccupied and frowning. Kent really loved the children. Could it be because of their mother? That did not make sense — not in view of Kent's friendship with her husband.

'Would you like her to look after you?' Simoni did glance up at that and her cheeks coloured enchantingly.

'Yes, we would,' from Vicki. 'She's kind; she let me sit on her knee.'

'Because Vicki was crying,' explained Catherine. 'I cried as well, but not as much as Vicki, because she's younger and she was frightened.'

'Frightened? Why was Vicki frightened?'

'It was that other lady who came for us at home. She

wasn't kind like that lady.'

'Don't point, Catherine.' Kent paused and then, 'You may call that lady Auntie Simoni.'

'That's a nice name!' Vicki twisted round to smile at Simoni. 'Are you my auntie?'

'Yes, she's your auntie.' Kent put them both down on the floor and called for Julia, who came at once. 'Put them to bed, Julia—'

'We haven't had any supper, Uncle Kent.'

'No? Well, we can't have you going to bed hungry. Julia will give you something.'

Obediently they went with Julia, but at the door Vicki turned.

'Can that nice lady— Can Auntie Simoni come up and kiss us good night?'

Kent glanced at her. She smiled and nodded.

'You've made a hit with Catherine and Vicki,' said Kent when they were sitting outside after dinner. 'You like children, that's obvious.'

'No one could possibly do anything but like those two. They're sweet.'

'Sweet. . . .' He nodded absently and fell into a thoughtful silence. Was he thinking that they might have been his? Simoni wondered, dejection stealing over her for no apparent reason, even though she was also baffled by the whole situation.

She and Kent were alone on the terrace, Bill and Martin having borrowed Kent's car and driven up to Bellapais to visit a friend of Bill's who had a summer residence there. Bill hadn't asked Simoni to accompany them and she was disconcerted at the idea of being alone with Kent Travers. However, there was nothing she could do about it and she decided to take advantage of the first opportunity offered and make her escape, saying she was tired and wished to go to bed early. It seemed, however, as the evening went on, that it would not be necessary to escape from Kent, for the conversation flowed without the strain she had expected, Kent's attitude towards her being freer than ever before. Perhaps it was because he was no longer her superior, she concluded, although for herself she still felt she should extend to him the utmost respect. In any case on flight he would be the one in command; as captain of the aircraft his word would be law from the moment of departure until they returned to Nicosia, and even his friend Bill would have to obey that word.

'So we fly together again,' he had just said, and his tone, edged with faint humour, was plainly designed to remind Simoni of past experiences. This brought a slight flush to her cheeks as she expressed the swift and fervent hope that nothing would go wrong.

'I used to think you put a hoodoo on me.' With this final sentence she spoke her thoughts aloud, almost unconsciously.

'You thought that?' He looked amazed but not unduly indignant. 'Did you never make blunders before?'

'I told you I didn't. Captain Holmes also remarked on my efficiency – if you remember?'

'So he did.' Kent eyed her with faint mockery, and said, rather too quietly, 'Perhaps you and he had more in common than we did.'

She glanced swiftly at him. What was he insinuating? Was he recalling her wholehearted response to his kiss and considering her cheap? Her flush spread;

she saw the amusement reflected in his eyes and glanced away, giving her attention to the view with exaggerated concentration. The garden was drenched in a silver radiance which spread down the hillside and across the sea to the Taurus Mountains, silhouetted against the soft purple velvet of an Anatolian sky. Closer to, and in a different direction, a myriad of golden lights twinkled from the tiny Cypriot villages nestling in the foothills of the limestone Kyrenia Range, graceful and gentle, contrasting greatly with that other Cyprus massif, the mighty Troodos Range, constructed of igneous gabbros and olivines and situated on the southern part of the island.

'You're very quiet, Simoni.' The words were spoken softly, yet they almost made her jump, for the night was so silent, steeped – as on another occasion – in sheer magic. Her flesh tingled; she donned a garb of cautious restraint.

'I was simply admiring the scene,' came the light response. 'The Turkish mountains are incredibly clear.'

Taking his eyes from her flushed face, he glanced across the waters.

'They are clear tonight. But then there's a full moon.' He rose at length and said, 'I'm taking a stroll before I turn in. Are you coming?'

Silence; tense and electrified. This situation was all too reminiscent of that other.

'No – I'm rather tired. I think I'll go to bed.'

He shrugged. 'Just as you like.' He made to walk away and her heart sank. Angrily she endeavoured to rally. She had no desire to walk with him, to experience a repetition of the incident which had resulted – for

Simoni – in an overwhelming sense of shame and self-contempt. No, certainly she did not wish to walk with him. After taking a few steps Kent turned, perception in his unsmiling eyes. 'Come on, Simoni. What are you afraid of?'

Her mouth went dry and she swallowed, angry with Kent and with herself, with her mind and her body because they were all doing the wrong things. She fell into step beside him. He pointed to the black entrancing silhouette of palms against the sky and instead of his hand returning to his side it came to rest on her shoulder. Her heart jerked and thudded. Her cloak of restraint must at all costs be maintained, she told herself, frantically aware of the wild uncontrol of her pulse. They walked in silence through the grounds and on to the silent twisting road. The silver luminance of the soft idyllic landscape, the slender cypresses on the hillside . . . placid mountains and the smiling shore, the dark unmoving sea, the heady air saturated with exotic perfumes. In the distance the complaining cry of a donkey and the music of sheep bells floating through the still clear night.

In desperation Simoni clung to her restraint. But the touch of Kent's hand could not be ignored; it thrilled and frightened her.

'Shall we turn back?' He broke the silence at last, but not the spell. Her voice was unsteady as she replied,

'Yes, it m-must be getting l-late.' Her little stammer caught his attention. He stopped and gazed down at her, tall and magnificent and dangerously masculine.

'What are you afraid of?' he repeated in some amusement. He was playing with her, she knew, and twisted away, her nerves springing to the alert even while the spell still remained unbroken.

'Afraid?' She gave a cracked little laugh. 'Why should I be afraid?'

'That,' he said, 'is what puzzles me.'

'Puzzles you?' she echoed, sidetracked momentarily and forgetting that her question had been meant to disabuse him about the fear he mentioned.

A soft laugh escaped him. 'Well, you're not exactly a little innocent, are you?'

Her face flamed. 'How dare you say that! And how do you know what I am?'

He quirked an eyebrow. The gesture seemed to convey his willingness to share her little game. She fumed on realizing this and, turning, would have ran from him, but her wrist was suddenly caught in a grasp that brought her round to face him.

'You're a tantalizing little devil, Simoni—' His lips found hers, holding them despite her struggles. But he gained no response this time, neither from her lips nor her body, even though he had her close, as on that other occasion. She stopped struggling and for a second her passivity deceived him. But she fought her natural desire – and won. Kent's tactics changed; he became gentle, his lips and arms caressing rather than demanding, but Simoni remained immune to this persuasion, subtle and persevering though it was. At last he held her from him, frowning darkly. Something in his manner now puzzled her; he seemed himself to be practising restraint.

'Why no response?' His tones snapped like trodden ice and the mocking amusement was no longer present in his eyes. They pierced her, probing for enlightenment. 'You responded once.'

She coloured, sending him a resentful glance. But her voice, coming over the clear air, was as cold as his own.

'Does it not occur to you that it's ungentlemanly to voice that reminder?'

His brow lifted. 'But how frigid! And how formal.' And he shook his head because of her expression and the hurt he saw and the moisture sparkling on her lashes. 'Ungentlemanly, is it?' His musing tones were faintly tinged with surprise. 'Are you trying to tell me I'm mistaken in you?'

She quivered all over. 'I hate you,' she said softly, and turned away from him.

'That's the second time you've told me that.' His voice held an odd inflection and she could not resist coming round again in order to look up into his face. This change ... this shedding of the guard of reserve which had always put him on a higher plane than herself, illustrating the superiority of his position ... what did it mean? He was distant still, granted, but human, somehow, and prone to certain human weaknesses. Her thoughts strayed to Ian's wife. Uncannily Kent said, 'You also told me I kissed you because you resembled my ex-fiancée.'

'Which was true.'

A faint smile touched his lips. 'You think so?'

'I'm sure of it.'

He sighed then and looked at her, turning up her face just as she began to lower it.

'You do resemble her, Simoni—'

'I know—' She stopped, but then, realizing she must now explain, she went on to tell him she had seen the photograph in Catherine's locket.

'And that set you wondering what it was all about?'

Simoni made no reply, naturally, and after a thoughtful pause he said, withdrawing his hand from under her chin, and returning to what he had been about to say before Simoni interrupted him, 'You're very much alike, and yet you're not alike—' He smiled at her and something twisted in her heart. That smile which had so softening an effect on the firm hard mouth . . . had she ever seen anything so attractive? To be married to such a man. . . . One would be forever experiencing little shafts of ecstasy. But one would be subdued as well, having always to know one's place. 'I wonder just how different you are?' He spoke these last words to himself, but their meaning was vividly portrayed. Catherine was false, untrustworthy; she had been – and still was – too fond of the men. After that first kiss Kent had concluded that Simoni was just as abandoned, but looking at his expression now she read doubt and knew instinctively that he was beginning to have second thoughts regarding his initial assessment of her character. Simoni forgot his treatment of her because the idea suffused her with warmth and her eyes shone suddenly and a tremulous smile quivered on her lips. Kent regarded her with an odd expression as for a long while they stood there in silence. And then, with an abruptness that startled her, 'As you remarked, it's late. Let's get back to the house.'

CHAPTER SIX

As they were having breakfast the following morning Kent explained to his guests that he would be out for several hours at least.

'I have things to do for Ian and then see that the house is closed up for the time being.' His voice was harsh, his face set in almost savage lines. No doubt about it, the thought of Catherine appeared to inflame him. 'I'll see that my secretary brings all the children's clothing,' he added, looking at Simoni. 'You mentioned last night that she had brought only their night clothes?'

Simoni nodded. Thora hadn't even thought to bring them a change of socks, although Simoni refrained from mentioning this.

'I was wondering,' Kent was saying, 'if you'd entertain them this morning, Simoni, as Julia does have her work to do? I'll get someone else in to help, but that will have to wait for the present. The children seemed quite happy with you, so I thought you might take them on the beach. Would you do that?'

'Of course,' she returned eagerly, a lightness sweeping over her because Kent had requested this of her and because of his comments and his sudden smile. 'I'll enjoy looking after them.'

The children had no beach clothes. but their ordinary briefs were sufficient and once on the sands Simoni stripped them both of everything but these.

'I can swim,' Catherine told her, going straight into

the water. 'Vicki can nearly swim, but she needs holding because she's frightened of sinking.'

'Then we shall have to hold her, shan't we?'

'You can, Auntie Simoni, but I'm going to have a good swim – right out there!'

'Not right out there, Catherine. Stay close to Vicki and me, there's a pet.'

'All right—' Catherine took a forward dive and the next moment she was swimming strongly, thoroughly enjoying herself. 'See, I told you I could swim!'

After a while they came out and sat on the sands. Simoni's gaze moved from one child to the other, trying to fix some slight resemblance to their mother, but she could not. They both had black hair and brown eyes, their faces were round and chubby and they both had attractive little upturned noses.

'Can we have some ice-cream?' Vicki pointed to the vine-shaded café away across the sands and Simoni took up her beach bag.

'You shouldn't ask,' admonished Catherine, and added, 'It's because she's young, Auntie Simoni. Vicki doesn't know it's rude to ask for things.'

Vicki's brow puckered in a frown. 'Why is it rude? If I don't ask for an ice-cream Auntie Simoni won't know I want one.'

Simoni laughed and handed each child a coin. 'Off you go!'

'Don't you want one?'

'Not just now, Catherine. Later, perhaps.'

Simoni watched them, flying like the wind towards the café where one or two people sat at the tables, thankful for the shade provided by the vines. How these vines would be missed in countries like Cyprus,

thought Simoni. They grew like weeds, swiftly and ac-
commodatingly, providing shelter from the merciless
sun and giving forth their delicious fruit into the bar-
gain. Vines often grew wild, and many times Simoni
had gathered grapes on a wayside bank or in a field.
The children became lost to sight and Simoni waited a
little anxiously until they reappeared, waving to her
now as they began to run back.

'Mine was fifty mils,' gasped Catherine, flopping
down beside Simoni. 'But Vicki wanted to save some
money, so hers was only twenty-five!'

'The man said yours was a bob.' Vicki sat down on a
towel and took her wafer from its loose wrapping.
'Catherine told the man you don't have bobs now, but
he said he'd learnt to say bob when he was a soldier and
he likes calling it a bob.' Vicki examined her wafer
before putting it to her mouth. 'The man said mine was
a tanner.'

'And I told him we don't have tanners any more, but
he just grunted and said to Vicki, "There you are, little
girl, a tanner change".'

Simoni smiled. Cyprus money was of the same value
as English money, and their coins were the same size.

'Are you coming for another swim?' Catherine asked
eagerly when the ice-cream had disappeared.

'Very well.' Simoni got up and took off her sun-
glasses.

'What about my money?' Vicki held it out. 'I'll lose
it.'

Taking it from her, Simoni put it in her bag.

'Come on, then, we'll have a race!' She waited until
the children had shot away and then began to follow.
but Vicki had stopped suddenly and now she was run-

ning in another direction.

'Uncle Kent!' A moment after the cry rang out Vicki was in Kent's hands, being tossed up aloft and caught again, squealing with feigned terror.

'You're back early.' Simoni spoke as Kent reached her. 'You said you'd be away all the morning.'

Putting Vicki down, Kent smiled quizzically as he said,

'Do you know the time?'

'No, but it's not—'. She looked startled, because of his expression. 'What time is it?'

'Half past one.'

Her eyes widened. 'Really?'

'Really.'

'Why didn't you bring your trunks?' Catherine wanted to know, taking hold of Kent's hand. 'You could have come for a swim with us then.'

'You've finished swimming for the present, young lady. Don't you ever get hungry?'

'We've had ice-cream!'

'Where are your clothes?' Kent looked round and Vicki pointed to them, neatly folded on top of Simoni's beach bag.

'There.'

'Go and put them on.' The two children raced away and Kent stood for a moment, looking down at Simoni. 'Thank you,' he said in quiet tones. 'I'm grateful to you, Simoni.' But she was shaking her head.

'I've thoroughly enjoyed myself.' She gave a little shrug. 'The time's flown, which is proof enough.'

'I suppose it is.' His glance flickered over her and she looked away, avoiding his eyes.

'I'll get my dress. . . .' She moved and he followed.

Picking up her dress, Simoni slipped her arms into it and began buttoning it up. Kent went down on one knee to fasten Vicki's sandal straps. Simoni looked at his dark head and powerful neck. He was too disturbingly close and she moved away just as he straightened up again. Her action brought on a slight nervousness in case Kent had observed it and made a guess at the reason for it. He would be enlightened then, as to his own power over her emotions, and from that knowledge he would derive exceeding amusement and, probably, satisfaction as well. The next moment Simoni was chiding herself for her fancies. It was most unlikely Kent would have noticed her action, and certainly beyond the bounds of possibility that he would attach any particular importance to it if he did. Yet how strangely he looked at her, his grey eyes probing, demanding even, as if they would by their expression force a revelation of her thoughts. Picking up the towels, Simoni folded them and pushed them into her bag.

'I'll take that,' said Kent surprisingly as Simoni was about to slip the handles over her arm.

'Thank you.'

The children placed themselves between the two adults and held their hands.

'Quite the little family, aren't we?' Kent laughed, and turned his head.

Simoni nodded, her pulse fluttering. She was relieved when Catherine spoke, asking Kent if he had his car.

'It's over there.' Kent jerked his head, indicating the car park.

'Oh, yes, I see it. Under the vines. You have to put it

in the shade, don't you, Uncle Kent, because of the sun? Daddy always puts his under the shade and so does Mummy—' She broke off, and darting Kent a glance Simoni noticed the tightening of his jaw and the sudden appearance of anger lines at the sides of his mouth. 'Uncle Kent, is Mummy coming back? Daddy says she isn't – not any more.'

A deep sigh and then, rather gently,

'We'll just have to wait and see, Catherine.'

'Can we stay with you and Auntie Simoni until Daddy comes out of hospital?'

'You'll be staying with me, Catherine, but Auntie Simoni doesn't live in Cyprus and she has to go home quite soon.'

Vicki tilted her head right back. Simoni found herself smiling despite the pathos of the situation, for the child looked so tiny against the mountain of a man beside her.

'I don't want Auntie Simoni to go home. Why can't she stay with us?'

'Will you?' put in Catherine before Kent could reply.

'I'd like to, Catherine,' Simoni answered softly. 'But that isn't possible.'

'Why?'

'As Uncle Kent has just told you, Catherine, I have to go home.' It was the first time ever Simoni had used Kent's Christian name and it came out so naturally that Kent himself did not seem to notice.

Vicki frowned. 'Why do you have to go home? Don't you like it here?'

'I like it very much – but I can't stay, for all that.'

They had reached the car and Kent opened the rear

door.

'In you get, and don't touch the door handles.'

'Is there any likelihood of their touching them?' About to get into the front seat, Simoni hesitated. 'Shall I sit with Catherine and Vicki?'

Kent shook his head, slipping Simoni's bag into one corner of the back seat.

'No, they won't touch the doors, but I always give them a reminder.'

'Always?' The word was out before Simoni realized it might savour of curiosity on her part. Kent started the car, appearing not to notice anything amiss with the question.

'I take them out sometimes,' was all he said, but Simoni cast him a sideways glance of surprise. Who would ever have thought the formidable Captain Kent Travers would concern himself with two little girls?

After lunch Catherine and Vicki were given into the care of Julia for an hour or two while the four adults discussed the trip to the desert. Kent had agreed to take them on Thursday and as today was Tuesday they still had about thirty-six hours in Cyprus as his guests. Once the discussions came to an end Bill and Martin said they were taking a siesta.

'You are? I was going to ask if you were coming for a dip. I'm taking the children on to the beach.' Kent's glance fell on Simoni. 'Are you taking a siesta?'

'No—'

'Then come along. The children will want you.'

The beach was practically deserted, as it had been earlier, and no sooner had Simoni undressed the children than they were off. Kent went after them, but Simoni lay on the hot sand, revelling in the sunshine.

After a while Kent waved and beckoned and she went into the water. It was the colour of a peacock's tail and ‚as smooth and limpid as a lake. Simoni floated lazily on her back, staring up at the incredibly blue sky on which was etched, in the far distance, a few motionless streaks of fair-weather cirrus cloud.

Squeals and protests brought her head round. Kent had Vicki on his back and he was threatening to toss her into the water.

'I'll drown!' But there was no fear in the child's voice. 'No, Uncle Kent – don't let me fall!'

'I wouldn't care if I fell in. Can I come on your back, Uncle Kent?' Catherine was beside him, endeavouring to scramble up, and clinging to the elasticated waist of his trunks. Kent helped her up and she was soon on his back. Simoni watched, fascinated, her emotions stirred and a strange yearning enveloping her. What a wonderful father he would make … and yet he was a confirmed bachelor, or so it was generally believed. Turning over, Simoni swam for the shore and sat on the fringe of the water, her knees drawn up under her chin. After a while Kent came out with Vicki and Catherine and they went towards the car. He had gone for money, apparently, because when the children returned they raced over to the café. Kent sat down beside Simoni, his hair tousled and wet, his body muscular and sinewed and very brown.

'Those two should have been boys,' he laughed, watching them.

'You prefer boys?' The question just came; Simoni had no idea why she should have asked it.

'I like both kinds.' He paused a while and then, 'There's something very endearing about little girls, though. It's a pity they—' Kent broke off, but Simoni finished for him, her chin lifting slightly,

'—have to grow into women.'

'I didn't say that.' Suave and unrepentant were the words, yet tinged with humour.

'You almost did,' she ventured with surprising temerity.

'Which was undiplomatic, eh?' He turned his head and so did she. Again he was too close, but this time Simoni did not move away.

'You believe that all nice little girls like Catherine and Vicki grow up into women like – like—' Simoni checked herself even while she knew she had gone too far.

'Like their mother?' he finished harshly.

'I'm sorry. Now it's I who am being undiplomatic.' She expected him to censure her, if only by silence, but other than a pointed change of subject, he gave no evidence of being annoyed with her.

'I think we'll take Catherine and Vicki out to tea somewhere. It will be a treat for them.'

'That would be nice.' She was inordinately happy, even though it could be only a transient happiness which surely must leave behind a trail of hurt and longing.

They took the coast road, making for the village of Ayios Georgios, where Kent knew the proprietor of a *kafeneion*. He greeted Kent enthusiastically and on being introduced to Simoni gave her a broad smile and said, with the customary swift friendliness of the Cypriot,

'Welcome to our island, Simoni.'

'Thank you, Davos. I am very happy to be in your

island.'

'These two little children . . .?' With typical Cypriot curiosity Davos wanted to be put completely in the picture.

'Guests of mine, Davos. Their father's met with an accident and he's in the hospital at Nicosia.'

Davos frowned and looked pained at the same time.

'But this is sad. They have you, though, Mr. Kent, so that is lucky for them.' Kent and Simoni and the two children were seated on high stools and Davos wanted to know what they were drinking. 'It's on me,' he added, and Kent laughed.

'It's always on you, Davos. How do you make any money?'

Davos shrugged and spread his hands – a most expressive Cypriot gesture.

'I have my lemon groves,' he smiled. 'Why worry about money?'

'Where else in the world would you get people like these?' whispered Simoni when Davos had turned away to get the children bottles of lemonade. 'Of all the people I've met I like the Cypriots best. I think you're awfully lucky being able to live here.' She stopped and flushed a little because of the way Kent looked at her before he said, an odd expression in his voice,

'You yourself would like to live here, I take it?'

Vicki was swivelling round on her stool and Simoni automatically put out a hand to stop the gyrations.

'I would, yes, but it won't ever be possible.'

He fell silent and something about him puzzled her. He stared into space, frowning slightly, and she watched him through her lashes, curious and faintly expectant. However, Kent did not speak and the tenseness was relieved only when Davos said again,

'Mr. Kent, what are you drinking?' He had given the children a bottle of lemonade each, and a straw, and now he stood behind his counter, waiting. 'Simoni – will you have a brandy?'

'No, thank you, Davos—'

'Have a brandy!' he insisted.

'We want you to put on a tea for us,' interrupted Kent. 'Can we have it in the garden?'

'Of course you can have tea in the garden. Salads? – and meat and cheese?'

'Those will do fine.'

'Chips?'

'No chips, Davos.'

'Very well. But first you must have a drink.'

'I'll have a brandy, then. Simoni, you'd better have the same.'

While they sat there with their drinks Davos and his wife Margharita prepared the tea, setting out a white-clothed table under the shade of a tall carob tree. Flowers grew in profusion, but almost all were in pots. With all streams dry for most of the year Cyprus had no water to waste. And as it was on a meter everyone was naturally careful with it. There was no real shortage, of course, but water was certainly not abundant as it was in England. So flowers were very often found in pots, so that they could be kept alive using the minimum amount of water.

It was when they had finished their tea, and the children were playing some distance away, that Kent said,

'Ian will be in hospital at least four months.'

'So long!' Her face shadowed. 'How awful! You're having Catherine and Vicki for that time?'

'Certainly. My secretary's already looking for an extra help so that Julia can devote her time to the children.'

Although aware by now of his strange contrasts of nature Simoni was nevertheless amazed by what Kent had just said. Apart from anything else the cost to him was going to prove considerable.

'It's very kind of you to do this for your friend,' she murmured at length and a half-smile touched his lips.

'Out of character, is that what you're thinking?'

She flushed then and, being incurably honest she just had to say,

'You can't blame me if I'm surprised.'

He gave a soft and faintly sardonic laugh.

'So now that I'm no longer your superior you're speaking your mind?'

She nodded absently, her attention caught by the charming little pink and grey lizard darting about at her feet, attacking the unwary insects.

'I would always remember I'm a guest in your house,' she said at last, aware all at once that she should not have nodded in agreement to Kent's remark.

'And if you weren't?'

His persistence disconcerted her, as he probably meant it to.

'I don't really know your character, so I shouldn't pass an opinion.' She smiled at him in a sort of depricating manner which brought no response from his now unmoving countenance.

'You've seen me only at work, you mean?' The double edge to his words, and the quality of satire in his tone brought an enchanting tint of colour to her face, throwing into relief the delicate contours of her cheek bones, prominent and high.

'Mostly – mostly it's been at work.' Simoni lowered her lashes because of the memory which would undoubtedly be reflected in her eyes. Kent liked playing with her, that was evident; he drew pleasure from reminding her of that incident at the Gulf Hotel, even though *she* had reminded *him* it was not gentlemanly to do so.

'Mostly . . .?' He said no more, and she raised her face after a time and saw the glimmer of a smile enter his eyes. But he was thoughtful, as if he might himself be going over what social occasions they had shared. These were few, owing to his reserve and his preference for the company of his own sex. When they were away from the base, staying at hotels abroad, Kent had almost invariably made it clear that he was not partial to women and when Simoni did happen to be in the same company as he she would often find herself totally ignored by Kent.

'Tell me,' he said after a long while, 'am I really such an ogre?'

She glanced quickly at him, a frown appearing between her eyes. She had the impression that there was rather more to the question than was apparent on the surface. It was as if he were wanting the information for future reference.

'You weren't very . . . kind. . . .'

The dark brows went up a fraction. 'Should kindness come into a job like ours?'

'Because of discipline, you mean? One can be a stickler for discipline and yet still be kind.'

Kent leaned back in his chair, but one hand remained on the table, a long slender hand, darkly contrasting with the snow-white tablecloth.

'You consider I was unkind simply because I complained – when I had a cause for complaint?'

She stirred uneasily and with a hint of impatience. Why these questions? It would almost seem that he wanted to vindicate himself, to convince Simoni he was not such a hard taskmaster as she had branded him.

But surely the arrogant Kent Travers would never be troubled about her opinion of him?

'I think you should have made allowances on those occasions when it wasn't entirely my fault.'

To her surprise he had no instant retort to make. On the contrary, Kent pondered over her words and then said,

'Perhaps you're right, Simoni. Maybe I should have been a little more understanding.' She stared at him unbelievingly. What an admission coming from the arrogant and normally infuriatingly sarcastic Kent Travers! 'Am I an ogre?' he repeated softly and curiously.

She glanced swiftly at him, her eyes twinkling in response to the glimmer of amusement in his.

'Not now,' came the instant retort, and Kent laughed. Simoni caught her breath and stared, unable to take her eyes from his face. If only he knew what he did to her when he laughed like that, or when he smiled in one particular way!

'You're very brave, Simoni.'

'It's pleasant to be in a position to retaliate,' she

returned, entering into his mood.

Kent cocked an eyebrow, saying softly, 'Do you know what I'd like to do right now?'

She laughed a trifle shakily, colouring up. 'Put the clock back . . .?'

'Indeed I would – just for a moment or two, so that I could put you in your place.'

'The day after tomorrow,' she reminded him, 'you'll be in a superior position again.'

'So I shall – and I'll remember this impudence.'

'And pay me back?' Simoni peeped at him from under her lashes; it was a distinctly coquettish action and the grey eyes flickered strangely. He didn't quite know how to take her, she decided, not without a small access of elation.

'With interest, perhaps,' drawled Kent at last, rising from his chair and glancing at his watch. 'Time we were on our way. Those children have been used to going to bed at half-past six.'

Bill and Martin were on the patio when they returned and the two girls ran to them.

'We've had a wonderful time!' exclaimed Catherine, going to Martin and standing by his knee. 'Guess where we've been?'

'To the beach, of course.' Martin smiled at the children in turn. 'Was the water nice and warm?'

'Lovely!' Not to be outdone, Vicki went and leant against Bill's knee. 'And we had tea out afterwards.'

'You did? Lucky blighters! Wish I had a nice uncle to take me out to tea.'

'Auntie Simoni came as well,' supplemented Catherine, turning to smile at her as she and Kent took possession of two spare chairs. 'It was just like when we went out with Mummy and Daddy sometimes – but it wasn't often with Mummy. Usually it was with Daddy or if he was working it was with Uncle Kent, but it's nicer when a lady comes too, isn't it, Vicki?'

'Yes, it's much nicer when a lady comes too.' Vicki turned to Kent and added, 'Can Auntie Simoni come with us again?'

'She's got to go home,' Catherine reminded her sister in flat tones that could not possibly pass unnoticed, and Kent threw Simoni a swift glance before, reaching up, he pulled a bell rope. Julia came at once.

'See to the children, Julia. They'll want a drink, and a biscuit, perhaps.'

'There's been a phone call for you, Mr. Kent,' Julia informed him as the children went obediently towards her. 'From Miss Thora. She wouldn't leave a message, but said the matter concerned the children's father and she would call here this evening about eight o'clock.'

'At eight? Then you'd better lay another place for dinner.' Kent was frowning heavily and the next moment he excused himself and went into the house. From where she sat Simoni could hear the questions he asked over the phone, but naturally she couldn't hear the answers. Kent was on to the hospital and his voice went grave as he asked his second question,

'This turn for the worse – it could be serious?' A silence at this end and then, 'Touch and go . . .?'

Kent's face was a mask of hate when he returned, but as Bill and Martin were talking only Simoni noticed this.

'Is Ian very ill?' she ventured when Bill and Martin had gone to their rooms to change for dinner. 'I ask because I couldn't help hearing your questions on the phone.'

He looked down at her in silence for a long preoccupied moment.

'Yes, Simoni, he's very dangerously ill. He has to have a special operation and I'm hoping to procure the services of a surgeon I know in London. He might be able to save Ian—' Kent broke off and his mouth was suddenly harder than she had ever seen it. 'If not I don't know what's going to happen to Catherine and Vicki.'

Simoni could not speak immediately because of the tightness in her throat. When at last she did manage to articulate words her accents were husky with concern.

'Their mother. . . .' Her voice trailed away into silence as she realized that the very mention of their mother must be as a red rag to a bull.

'I feel pretty sure,' he said between his teeth, 'that she'll never come near the children again.'

Thora arrived while the men were still in their rooms, changing, and she was shown into the salon where Simoni was standing by a small table on which stood a magnificently carved Chinese figure, obviously a rare treasure Kent had picked up on his travels. Simoni was admiring it, but turned as Thora and Julia entered.

'You have met.' Julia smiled at Simoni and made her departure.

'Good evening.' Thora spoke curtly, looking Simoni over in the most unmannerly way. 'Where is Kent?'

'In his room, changing. He shouldn't be long.'

Thora sat down on the couch, her eyes still on

Simoni. 'You're leaving here tomorrow, Kent tells me?'

'That's right,' came the non-committal reply. Simoni resented the way the girl looked at her, almost as if she, Thora, were the mistress of the house and Simoni an uninvited guest.

'It must have been a bother to Kent – having to accommodate you all, with these two children having been thrust on him just now.'

Simoni did not know how to conduct a conversation with the girl, for she appeared to be completely lacking in tact.

'I don't suppose he would have extended the invitation had he not meant us to accept it, Miss Benson.' Simoni returned at last, glancing with relief to the door as it opened and Kent walked into the room.

'Ah, Kent!' A glow entered Thora's eyes and reflected itself in her dazzling smile. 'I hope you didn't mind my not leaving a message? I felt you would wish me to convey my news to you directly.'

He smiled down from his great height; with a truly feminine gesture Thora tipped back her head and clasped her hands together. She looked like a suppliant worshipping at a shrine and Simoni knew a sudden dart of contempt. The girl would bend on one knee for attention, Simoni felt sure . . . and the arrogant and lordly Kent Travers would probably enjoy the role of master to a slave.

He caught Simoni's eye, read her thoughts and faintly smiled, obviously amused by what he saw.

'As a matter of fact, Thora, I rang the hospital and they told me the news.'

A swift sideways glance at Simoni, and then, 'Could

we talk privately, Kent?'

Surprisingly he shook his head, disconcerting her.

'I see no necessity for that. Miss Clarke knows why the children are here, knows Ian is dangerously ill in hospital.'

Flushing at Kent's quick refusal to accede to her request, Thora cast an invidious glance in Simoni's direction. It would appear, decided Simoni, that Thora blamed her for the snub.

'I was going to make a suggestion about the children,' began Thora a trifle hesitantly. 'I know of someone who has a small boarding-school—'

'Thanks for your interest, Thora,' Kent broke in shortly. 'But Catherine and Vicki wouldn't be happy in a boarding-school. In any case, I've promised Ian that I'll take care of them here until he comes out of hospital – until he's well enough to make his own arrangements, in fact.'

Thora looked hard at him. 'You believe he'll come out.'

'I hope he'll come out, Thora,' was the soft but harsh response.

'Matron said he needs to have a very serious operation and that he might not get over it.'

'If I manage to get the man I want – in time – Ian will recover all right.'

After dinner, when they were all on the patio drinking coffee, Bill once again scraped his chair close to that of Simoni and slipped an arm across her shoulders. The action caught Thora's eye; she turned deliberately to Kent, as if she would draw his attention to it. But Kent was already aware of it and his grey eyes glinted. Simoni flushed, angry with Bill and yet more angry with herself for allowing Kent's opinion to trouble her.

Thora left just after eleven; Kent offered to walk to the car with her and Simoni bade him good night before he went, saying she was going to bed.

On his return she was standing on her balcony, gazing out towards the sea, enjoying the cool tranquil night after the heat of the day. The moon was high, brilliant and positive above the purple fluted outline of the Kyrenia Range, that gentle chain of mountains bordering the sea-line for practically the whole of the northern coast. From two of its towering summits twinkled the lonely lights of the castles of Hilarion and Buffavento, romantic both in their situation and their history. Lower down on the smiling foothills could vaguely be discerned the shadowed terrain inhabited by olive trees and carobs, with here and there a tall straight date palm darkly etched against a sky of amethyst and pearl.

Simoni heard Bill and Martin say their good nights and retire to their respective rooms. Then a shadow across the terrace betrayed the presence of the man who now disturbed her thoughts too greatly by far, his image lingering all the while, tantalizing, persistent, refusing to be suppressed or even treated with indifference.

Instinctively Simoni made to withdraw into her bedroom but, glancing up as if he sensed her presence, Kent hesitated, then stopped in an attitude of thoughtfulness. And after a moment or two had elapsed he turned decisively, making his way towards the steps leading up from the garden to her balcony.

Something wrenched at her heart-strings, jerking

them uncomfortably; she desired only to flee from the tall approaching figure negotiating the steps with a sort of easy feline grace, taking them two at a time. What did he want, coming to her like this out of the mothy half-light of the garden? Nerveless fingers quivered on the balcony rail, evidence enough of her inner agitation. Why didn't Kent leave her alone? Why this interest all of a sudden?

'May I come up?' Prosaic tones and request. He was up, she wished to point out, but her throat was dry and she could manage only a husky,

'Of course.'

He stood closer to her in the deep silence, the pure and absolute silence of a violet, moon-sprayed night, his darkly outlined profile clear-cut and forbidding.

'Simoni,' he began after some small hesitating, 'I'm putting a proposition to you, and I would ask that you give it some consideration. By that I mean – don't make me the impulsive answer which must inevitably seem the one you should give, which is an instant refusal of my proposition.' He turned to her, his face grave in the moonlight. 'I'm fully aware of what I'm asking of you, and all I can say is that you won't lose by it, not in any way. I'm asking you to consider looking after these two little girls until their father comes out of hospital—' He stopped and she thought she detected a few beads of perspiration on his brow. 'Ian's chances of survival are remote, Simoni, but not impossible.' He still stared at her, holding her gaze squarely. 'Should he die the position would be permanent. Should he live and decide to take the children to his sister in England – he has mentioned this to me – or should their mother return, which I consider most unlikely, you'll be without a job, having lost this one you're holding now. However, I have influence in certain quarters and I can assure you there'd be another post available, similar to the one you have.'

Simoni just stood there, mentally going over all he had so calmly and unemotionally said. And borne in on her was the knowledge that all his previous questions and apparent anxiety concerning her opinion of him had been the prelude to this request. As he had stated, her impulse was to make an instant refusal, because of her job and the pleasure she derived from it. She had worked hard to obtain such a post, and knew she was fortunate to have landed it without the slightest trouble or anxious period of waiting. So smoothly had everything gone for her that she should not for one moment be contemplating an acceptance of Kent's offer. But she was contemplating an acceptance. Yet surely it would be a dangerous situation, her feelings for Kent being what they were. To remove herself from his magnificence, to break the power he unconsciously held over her emotions ... this was the path of common sense. . . .

Kent stirred beside her and instant fire shot through her veins, depriving her of rational thought.

'I don't know. . . .' Frail words, reflecting weak resistance which she fervently wanted to conceal. And then by sheer force of will-power she cried, 'No, I can't! I would be out of my mind to throw up my—'

A hand on her arm checked her; she looked down at it, its warmth adding strength to the fire within her.

'Naturally I don't expect your answer immediately.' The soft words were subtly persuasive and it seemed incredible that his icy sarcasm had ever sent her cheeks aflame and her nerves fluttering. 'It will do when we return on Saturday.'

'It would be most imprudent,' she began, her voice low, echoing her silent plea, 'Don't tempt me, Kent, please don't tempt me.' 'I'd never get another job like the one I have,' she murmured aloud.

'I said I have influence. Should you decide on this sacrifice – and it's for the children, Simoni, not for me – then naturally I shall make quite sure you're not the loser.'

Uncertainty again ... but no. It was only assumed uncertainty, created by her desperation to combat the yearnings of her heart and prudently take heed of the whisperings of common sense. She owned reluctantly that real uncertainty had never for a moment held her thoughts.

'I do feel for the children. ...' Her voice tailed off and she turned to look at him, her great eyes troubled, and Kent, believing he knew the reason for this, repeated almost gently,

'Give me your answer on Saturday. Think about the matter over the next couple of days—' He broke off as a thought struck him and asked, in a totally different tone of voice, 'Bill? Is there some understanding between you?'

She shook her head.

'No, he's just my boss.'

A small pause and then, still in the rather curt tones which had replaced the previous softness,

'You're sure?'

'Quite sure.' He appeared to be considering this – treating it with scepticism? she wondered, reflecting on the way Bill had twice put himself close to her with the deliberate intention of encircling her shoulders with his arm. It was suddenly important that Kent believe her and she turned to him with impulsive urgency. 'I'm speaking the truth.'

His dark head turned; she saw his expression and breathed again.

'I don't doubt your word, Simoni.'

She smiled swiftly; it was a smile of thanks which brought a shade of amusement to his eyes.

'Is it so important?' he inquired, lifting an eyebrow.

'Is – is what important?' she countered, and he laughed at her wile.

'That I believe you – you know what I'm talking about.'

She glanced away, disconcerted, and bewildered as well. And yet she should not be surprised by this change in his manner with her. After all, he had just asked a favour of her – a great favour because it meant a complete upheaval in her life and her plans. So naturally he must treat her with civility and consideration.

'It's very late,' Kent observed, glancing at his wrist watch. 'We have to be up early in the morning, so we'd better turn in.'

'Yes.' She didn't want to go to bed, not yet, and with the admission of this an audible sigh left her lips. Kent heard it with some surprise.

'What was that for?'

She shrugged; it was a nervous gesture for an honest reply was not possible.

'It's such a lovely night,' she murmured at last, rather lamely.

'You mean, it's a shame to go in?' Soft the question and exploratory. Simoni's nerves became alert and taut and a shaky laugh fell on the still warm air.

'We'll have to go in?' she quivered. 'We can't – can't—' To her consternation Kent reached up and snapped on the light. It was in order to read her expression, apparently, judging by the way he observed her. Naturally she endeavoured to avoid too thorough an examination, but her intention was foiled as a slender brown finger touched her chin, forcing it up. She met Kent's gaze then because she had to and her heart thudded so that she felt sure he must hear it. What was this torture? Was it intentional? Could it be possible that he sensed her feelings and in consequence enjoyed this taunting game?

'So you don't want to go in . . .?' He spoke softly, almost to himself. 'Just as I thought.' And he bent his head and kissed her quivering lips, so gently, and without the driving force that had previously tempted her, demanding surrender. Presently he leant away, his keen observation taking in her fluctuating colour and the shy and changing light in her expressive eyes. Simoni brought down her long lashes, lest he should read what was in her heart. 'You know, Simoni, you're something of a puzzle,' he said at length, a good deal amused by her defensive action. 'One minute you invite me to stay out with you and the next you're so timid you might be no more than an inexperienced schoolgirl.'

Her instinct was to seize on that, and indignantly deny it, but she checked herself, aware that it was half true. For while she had not categorically invited him to stay out with her, she had undoubtedly wanted him to

113

do so. He still held her and she became wrapped in the warmth and strength of his hands on her arms. A faint breeze moved the vast stillness, murmuring down from the graceful line of the Kyrenian peaks to sway the palms and rustle the leaves of eucalyptus trees on the edge of the garden. The light from the balcony revealed the pomegranate trees smouldering in the hedge and the brilliant trumpets of the hibiscus growing up the side of the far verandah. On the breeze floated the intoxicating perfume of roses mingling with the sweet and subtle scent of oleanders. From a mountain village a long way off drifted the haunting strains of *bouzouki* music and, diverted for a moment, Simoni frowned in puzzlement.

'Is that coming from a *taverna*?'

'No; there's a wedding up in the village of Klepini. This is the first day; it'll be going on for another couple of days, I expect.' The sea glistened in a shower of moonlight and a million points of crystal flickered from the great vault of the heavens. Suddenly Kent became interested and Simoni looked up to see the star sailing across the sky. They both watched for a while before Kent said, laughing,

'The magic shattered. It's a sputnik.'

Simoni nodded. No shooting star ever travelled at such a relatively slow pace. 'Good night, Simoni – and don't forget to think about my proposition.' The next moment he was gone, and after snapping off the light Simoni entered her room and softly closed the balcony doors.

CHAPTER SEVEN

'SIMONI, you can take the right-hand seat.' The order was given curtly as they boarded the aircraft at Nicosia Airport. On a job of work now, Kent adopted the old familiar manner towards her, his face unsmiling. It was just like old times, reflected Simoni – except, of course, that she had never before sat in this particular seat. Bill was at the back and Martin occupying the rear seat by the large window.

Kent called the tower for start clearance.

'Nicosia approach, Nicosia approach. Gulf Alfa Tango Alpha Hotel calling Nicosia approach on two one decimal two. Do you read?'

'Gulf Alpha Tango Alpha Hotel, Nicosia approach read you loud and clear, hear me.'

'I read you loud and clear too. Request start clearance.'

'Your clear start, Gulf Alpha Tango. The outside air temperature is plus one-five and the Q.N.H. one-zero, one-seven.'

Kent started the engines and then requested taxi clearance.

'Alpha Hotel, Nicosia approach. Request taxi clearance and instructions, please.'

'Roger; Alpha Hotel your taxi clearance confirmed. Runway two seven, left hand.'

The aircraft taxied round, Kent checking his instruments again as he did so. A short while later he was given the instructions.

'Roger; Alpha Hotel, you're clear, line up and take-off. Wind two-nine-zero, five knots.'

The throttles were eased slowly forward, increasing the power, and Kent made another cursory survey of his instruments. With the customary vibration the aircraft rose from the ground, and within seconds it was fully airborne.

There were several stops on the flight for refuelling and it was several hours later that Simoni noticed the frown appear on Kent's face.

'Anything wrong?' she asked a trifle breathlessly.

The radio compass wasn't working, he told her, and he was now taking his readings from a small compass he always carried.

By midday they were over the desert. Martin took his photographs on instructions from Bill, who pointed out to Simoni the little rises – anticlines – which often gave indication of the presence of oil. Simoni was thrilled with the work, avidly taking lessons from Bill in his surveys of the terrain. It was arid and for the most part featureless, with the blazing sun searing over the ochre-coloured landscape.

They still had some considerable distance to fly when Martin was suddenly taken ill. His breathing was difficult and his face took on a purplish tinge. Simoni went to him, giving him a few drops of brandy.

There was a spare seat, so Bill moved and they laid Martin down as best they could. But he was suffering considerable discomfort and Kent decided to land. He turned to Simoni.

'You can map-read, I suppose?'

'Of course.'

'There's a topo here – sort out where we are. I've

drawn the line of flight plan; you'll see a little landing field somewhere hereabouts.' He pointed to the line on the topographical map. 'I'm going down there – that's the line we're following. There are one or two landmarks you'll be able to pick out. Just let me know if I'm on track or off track – or to starboard or port.'

Simoni looked at the map several times and looked down, a rather worried frown appearing between her eyes.

'I can't recognize anything down there. According to the map there should be a bit of rocky ground—' She shook her head. 'There doesn't appear to be anything to correspond with the features on the map.'

Kent looked down. 'What's that? There's a piece of rocky ground.'

That wasn't it, Simoni felt sure.

'I can't see the features you mention. In fact, there doesn't—'

He gave a small sigh and Simoni broke off. Kent Travers on duty was a very different man from the Kent Travers who had been with her on the balcony last night.

'If you can't read it, say so,' he snapped impatiently. They were using up fuel, she knew, and could fully understand his anxiety. 'There's a hill over there—' He indicated the spot on the map. 'Look for the old wadi – it's in this vicinity. I've seen it many times.'

A long silence followed while Simoni tried to correlate the physical features depicted on the map with something on the ground. Reluctantly she shook her head.

'The – the landmarks round here aren't at all distinct,' she ventured nervously, a terrible suspicion entering her head. Kent seemed not to hear; he was looking around, his brow furrowed and his mouth tight. Was he thinking the same as she?

'Kent. . . .' His name came out unconsciously as the map in her hand fluttered. 'I think we're off course.'

'Think? We *are* off course! Now how the hell has that happened—'

'Kent,' urgently from Bill, 'Martin's in a bad way.'

'No, I'm not.' Getting up, Martin staggered to the seat behind Kent. 'I want air, that's all. I'll be fine now.'

Kent looked at Simoni. What difference could a seat make? he was questioning silently.

'I think it's a heart attack.' Simoni merely framed the words for Kent to see. He nodded.

'I'll land,' he said with decision. 'In any case, we can't go on like this. We'll run short of fuel. Fix your harnesses.' He made a reconnaissance survey for a likely place to land.

'There are a great many boulders,' began Simoni, and then stopped. Kent knew what he was doing. The whole area was boulder-strewn, but Kent had espied a small strip which appeared to be fairly free from obstructions. Making a low level circuit around the area, he turned downwind to make his landing, putting the undercarriage down. Simoni and Bill were tensed but unafraid. Martin was not capable of assimilating the drama of the moment. Anxiously Simoni watched the ground as Kent descended and prepared to land on his little chosen strip. He would make it quite safely—

'Martin!' Too late Bill shouted. The photographer had discarded his harness and slumped forward, throwing out his hands to grasp Kent's arms for support.

'What the devil—!' Kent had no chance to right his aircraft. It landed heavily on the starboard undercarriage, ripping it off, with the starboard main plane digging into a mass of boulders and tumbleweed. The nose twisted, buckling as the aircraft came to a grinding halt.

'Simoni, get that door open. And don't forget the water,' he added – which was quite unnecessary as far as Simoni was concerned. She knew better than to leave without taking with her two cans of water. Bill was off before her, also carrying water, while Kent took up Martin in his arms and transported him to a place some distance from the aircraft.

'Get upwind!' he thundered at Bill, who was walking downwind. 'If it bursts into flames you'll be—' Kent stopped and stared. 'What's wrong with you?'

'I – I—' Staggering back, Bill caught up with Kent and Simoni. 'My head – I bashed it on the radio rack.'

'You—?' Kent looked ready to explode. 'Wasn't your harness fixed?'

'I thought it was, but it mustn't have been. God, my head feels as if it's been hit with a sledgehammer!'

'It's bleeding very badly.' Simoni's eyes wandered to the plane; she would have risked returning for the first-aid kit, but knew she wouldn't get very far before an order from Kent brought her back.

After making Martin as comfortable as possible Kent turned his attention to Bill, his eyes glinting wrathfully. Bill's carelessness with his harness had resulted in their having two invalids on their hands instead of one.

'Have you anything I can use as a pad, Simoni?'

'No. . . . I've several handkerchiefs, but they're in my handbag—'

'They're no use there,' he snapped, cutting her short impatiently. 'I have a couple myself; they'll have to do for the present.'

'Sit still, both of you,' Kent ordered when he had finished. 'Moving about in this heat causes a very quick loss of water.'

The first thing was to rig up some form of shelter and as soon as Kent decided there was no risk of fire he and Simoni re-entered the aircraft.

'Do you want me to help with the tent?' asked Simoni. 'Or shall I attend to Bill's injury first?'

'You can help me with the tent – that's the most important matter at the moment.' He glanced at the dash, frowning. 'And then I want to find out how we came to be so far off track.'

He and Simoni fixed the tent, both working slowly so as not to perspire any more than was necessary. With the invalids made comfortable and Bill's wound dressed, Simoni went back to the aircraft to prepare a warm drink for the two men.

'Simoni, come here!' At Kent's sharp command she turned, nerves quivering for some reason she could not explain. But the tone of voice, and now his expression. . . .

'Yes?' She looked up at his face, bewildered and fearful.

'I presume that's your handbag?'

'Y-yes.' Her glance strayed to it, lying there on the

dash where she had put it after administering the brandy to Martin. It didn't immediately register that it was close to the compass. 'Yes, of course it's mine.'

'What have you inside it?' and before she could reply, 'Open it up and empty it out on here.'

She obeyed, still perplexed. A lipstick and powder compact, and two clean handkerchiefs, still folded. A small diary, the tiny brandy bottle and a tube of sun lotion. And of course, her purse.

Kent's lips were tight; he cast her an almost murderous glance before, leaning over, he picked up the powder compact, putting it near the compass, which began to swing violently. He then took it away and as she stared at the compass settling down to magnetic north again Simoni lifted a trembling hand to her cheek. She swallowed, trying to get rid of the blockage in her throat. Presently she said,

'It's all m-my fault?'

'Certainly it's your fault!' he thundered. 'Had you no more damned sense than to put your bag next to the compass? – knowing you had a metal object inside it? No wonder we're off track!'

'I'm sorry—' She stopped. An apology was totally inadequate, and useless. Kent was in no mood to listen, and she certainly could not blame him. She looked up, her hand still pressed to her cheek, her eyes far too bright. 'I always had a fear that something catastrophic would happen.' Her eyes strayed to the compass. 'And n-now it has.' She could not bear to look on Kent's face, so harsh and wrathful was his expression.

The men in the tent were suffering from shock and she hoped the drinks would help to settle their nerves.

She herself was drained, and very tired and unhappy, being unable to drag her thoughts away from the mistake she had made. The bag had been down at the side of her for the greater part of the flight, but when Martin was taken ill she had produced the brandy bottle which she had thoughtfully put in her bag and, in her frantic haste to give Martin the medicine, she had inadvertently tossed her handbag on to the dash. But it was a careless action, she frankly owned this to herself. It wasn't as if she didn't know that the compact could swing the compass, and set it on a wrong heading, but she hadn't given the matter a thought. In fact, it was only when Kent brought her attention to it that she realized her bag was on the dash.

'How do you feel now?' Simoni looked anxiously at Martin. He was lying down, his head resting on one of the seats which Simoni had brought from the aircraft.

'Much better. Simoni, I'm so dreadfully sorry. I'm entirely to blame for the crash, aren't I?'

The ghost of a smile touched her lips.

'There have been one or two unfortunate circumstances contributing to our plight, Martin. But it's not too serious. We're expected back at El Gizahalhad airport in a few hours' time and when we don't arrive they'll send out a rescue team to search for us.'

'The radio—' began Bill, but Simoni shook her head.

'The captain can't get a peep out of it, I'm afraid.'

Bill eyed her curiously. 'Aren't you afraid, Simoni?'

'Of course not. There's no reason why I should be. But I'm just terribly upset and very tired, Bill.' And when he would have asked for an explanation she added, 'I'm going to rest now, in the aircraft.'

She returned to it; Kent was still tinkering with the radio and Simoni sat down on one of the seats, staring at Kent's bent head.

'No use,' muttered Kent at length. He sounded exceedingly troubled, she thought, and asked,

'Our position isn't serious, is it? I mean, they'll be out looking for us a few hours from now.'

Kent twisted round and faced her. 'They'll be searching on the route where we should be,' he said in soft and even tones. 'I daresay that compass had swung twenty degrees or more off heading.'

Her face paled. She had not thought of that when reassuring the two men in the tent. She said haltingly,

'Our water . . . have we sufficient?'

'Sufficient for what?'

Simoni bit her lip. 'How l-long will it last?' she faltered, looking down at her hands, clasped together in her lap.

'Forty-eight hours – with strict rationing.'

'Two days—' She was suddenly afraid. 'That's n-not long.'

A small sigh and then,

'We'll begin to worry about that later. In the meantime we'd better decide on a plan of action.' He paused a moment. 'Those two can't be given duties yet awhile, so what has to be done must be shared between you and me. I'll remain on watch tonight, ready to light a flare should I hear anything. You'll see to the food and drink.'

She nodded. Kent would of course ration the food

and drink, as the captain of an aircraft always did in a situation such as this.

'Shall we have to fix up another shelter?'

'Later, yes, when the sun's gone down.'

Meanwhile, they all rested in the shade of the tent, so as not to lose excessive moisture from their bodies by unnecessary perspiration.

'How much water can we manage on?' Bill was curious to learn. 'One can go without food for very long periods, I do know that.'

'The bodily water requirements are always related to the existing conditions.'

'Yes, I see that. The hotter the climate the more water is required, because of course you lose more.'

'Quite, and so it pays to keep in the shade, so that your bodily water loss through perspiration and evaporation is minimized.'

He glanced at Simoni and she understood. They had sufficient water for two days at the rate Kent was rationing it. Two days. . . . Supposing they weren't rescued?

'My rationing will be stringent,' he said curtly, 'because although I have hopes of our being rescued within the next twelve hours or so, I'm not by any means sure of this, on account of our going so far off course.'

'How did we come to be off course?' Bill wanted to know. 'Was it the fault of the compass?'

Silence for a second or two and then Simoni spoke.

'It was my fault, Bill.' She went on to explain what had happened and saw that Bill was frowning at her. Should the situation become serious, she thought, these three men were going to hold her entirely responsible for any discomfort they might be called upon to endure.

So unhappy was she that after their meal she went into the aircraft and sat there alone. But soon Kent called her, sharply and imperiously, and she came out again and went to the tent where they were all resting.

'What are you doing in there?'

'Just sitting,' she shrugged.

'Then sit here. It's too hot in there.' This was true, of course, for the sun was pouring through the rear window of the plane. 'Nothing can be done with the aircraft or the radio. We can't do much at all to help ourselves.'

'We just have to wait?' Martin sat up, appearing to be completely recovered.

Kent nodded without replying and the four lapsed into a long silence, each busy with his or her own thoughts.

Darkness was falling; for the first time in her life Simoni had no appreciation of the sunset, made absolutely magnificent by the sand reflections. The descent of night was even more swift than in Cyprus and adjacent countries, there being only a mere fifteen minutes between full daylight and inky blackness. And as the sun sank so the temperature dropped, rapidly.

'You'd better move into the aircraft for the night,' Kent said, 'I'll stay in the tent.'

Simoni looked at him, deep anxiety in her eyes. 'You'll be frozen,' she murmured.

'Frozen?' Martin looked interrogatively at her, not

having much knowledge of desert conditions. 'It won't get all that cold, will it?'

Simoni nodded, explaining that the diurnal temperature range for this part of this particular desert was ten degrees centigrade.

'That's fifty Fahrenheit,' she added, 'so, as the daytime temperature was a hundred and ten, it will drop to sixty. And after the high daytime temperature you'll shiver at sixty.'

'But how does this happen?' Martin gave a rueful grin. 'I know I'm dense, but I can't imagine how it can get so cold in so short a time – I mean, because the sun's up at five – so I heard Kent remarking a while back.'

'In the desert you get this very rapid heating and cooling. Clear skies like this result in intense insolation – that is, the heating of the earth's surface by the sun. At night when the sun drops excessive radiation takes place and so low temperatures must result.' She flushed a little because of the expression on Kent's face; he was interested in what she was saying, but at the same time the harshness remained, so that she could not for one second forget her guilt.

'In other words,' Bill was saying, 'the earth rapidly loses the heat transmitted to it by the sun.'

'Very rapidly – in a dry region like this. Oceans of course retain the heat and so you have no great variations of temperature in countries bounded by great expanses of water.'

The conversation on climatology could have continued, but Kent said it was time Simoni and the two men went into the aircraft and made themselves as comfortable as possible. He would be in later to see to their rations, he said, with an accompanying glance at

Simoni which said that on no account was she to touch these things until he gave her permission to do so.

By noon the following day all four were worried, and by four o'clock in the afternoon, with another night looming up before them, Simoni decided to go to the aircraft, wishing to be on her own, for the periodic silences falling on the company seemed to her imagination fraught with condemnation and reproach. Their food was running out, but more important, the water position was now serious and Kent had said the rations would be reduced.

Kent had been perusing the topographical map and he told the two men he knew where they were, three hundred and fifty miles from El Gizahalhad airport. He made no direct speech with Simoni and she naturally never spoke a word, for her misery crushed her like a dead weight; she was sick inside and had no desire to speak to anyone. She went off, hoping to be alone for a few minutes before Kent called her back. The sun was slanting now, but the heat was still intense, casting a quivering haze over the vast parched and arid landscape. It was easy to see how one could go mad in such sweltering, featureless terrain; Simoni herself could have cried with the heat earlier in the day, and she felt she never wanted to see the sun again as long as she lived. . . . Never see the sun. Would they come out of this alive? Water was life; there could be no survival without it. . . . And their water was low, dangerously low.

She sat down; she had a terrible thirst but as yet there was no sign of any real discomfort. Bill on the other hand was flushed, she noticed, and had no appetite – the first symptoms of dehydration.

He had lost his patience, too, demanding another drink which, of course, Kent would not allow him to have. Simoni tried not to think of her own thirst, but it dragged along with her, and she was conscious of it the whole time. The others were suffering, and it was all her fault. Overwhelmed by her sense of guilt, Simoni put her head in her hands. Her shoulders shook, but she was dry-eyed.

'What is it?' Kent's voice, quiet and calm. She turned, searching his face.

'Are we? How much water have we?'

'Sufficient for another twenty hours.'

'And then?'

He shrugged. Words were unnecessary, and Simoni's lip quivered.

'It's all my fault.' Tears filled her eyes. 'If – if we're not rescued, then I'll b-be to blame for all – for all your deaths.'

To her surprise the shade of a smile appeared on Kent's lips.

'I shouldn't trouble yourself too much about that. You'll not be living with it on your conscience.' She said nothing and he continued, in a lighter tone, 'We're not all going to die.'

'How could I be so stupid?' she cried, shaking her head distractedly. 'It wasn't as if I were inexperienced. I should have known what would happen.'

He stood a while looking at her.

'What made you put your bag there? It couldn't have been there all the time, otherwise we'd have been off course long before we were.'

'It was when I took the brandy out for Martin. I was so frantic – he seemed to be dying – and I just didn't think. I must have flung the bag down. I don't even remember doing it.' She blinked to clear her vision. 'That's no excuse, of course, I'm fully aware of that.'

To her surprise he dropped a gentle hand on to her shoulder.

'This isn't the time for self-recriminations, Simoni,' he said. 'It was a natural mistake, I see that now, caused entirely by your anxiety over Martin. I could have made the same mistake myself—'

'Oh no, Kent—' She broke off, flushing at the use of his name. 'I'm sorry. . . .'

'Don't be. In a situation like this there's no room for formalities. As regards my making a mistake – I'm not infallible, Simoni. I could have made the same mistake – under these particular conditions.'

His admission surprised her, but it could not mitigate her anguish.

'Is there nothing we can do?' A stupid question and she lowered her head. They required water for survival, and their water was fast running out. 'Of course there isn't.'

A small silence followed and then Kent told Simoni what he had in mind.

'If there's no sign of rescue by six this evening I'm going to try and make for this wadi.' On the topographical map he indicated the river bed. Simoni glanced at the scale and made a rough calculation. 'It'll be dry, admittedly, but there could be water holes—'

'They're never easy to find,' she interrupted, terror in her heart. Kent walking alone in the desert, for fifteen miles. And if he didn't find water he would never get back. . . . 'You have to search for them. No, please don't go!'

Kent glanced up at her, his eyes flickering strangely.

'I'll have to go.' He looked down at the map and fell silent for a while. 'We'll go into the tent and talk in front of the others,' he said, and left the plane followed by Simoni.

Martin and Bill listened eagerly to what Kent had to say. Then Bill suggested he accompany him.

'I'd be only too thankful to have you,' admitted Kent, but shook his head. 'That wound isn't healed by any means and it could give you trouble. My task won't be easy as it is and I can't risk having you with me.' Kent turned his head as Martin would have spoken. 'And I'm afraid I can't take you, either,' was the firm response to the question which Martin had not even been given the chance to voice. 'No, I must go alone—'

'Take me,' interrupted Simoni on impulse. 'It will mean that if we do find water then we can bring back twice the quantity.'

'Twice?' He smiled, and as he lifted a brow, Simoni's face took on a self-deprecating expression.

'Two can certainly bring back more than one,' she amended.

'It would be too much for you, Simoni. No, I'll go alone.'

She knew what he was thinking. Should there be no water then he himself would be the only sufferer.

'Kent,' she faltered, oblivious of the curious expressions of Bill and Martin, 'if you don't find water you – you'll not get back.' The thought was agony –

unbearable. She *must* go with him.

He made no answer, knowing as well as she that the long trek would greatly increase his water requirement. If possible on desert survival one should rest, in the shade, at all times and so conserve one's water content.

'We'll be optimistic, Simoni,' he observed at last, 'and hope that water will be found.' He then went on to give them instructions. Bill was to look out for half the night and Martin the rest. On no account must they be tempted to take more water than the ration he now stipulated. And as the water was cut so must the food be cut. This was essential. He spoke to Simoni mostly, but she was only half listening and when at last she managed to get in a word she said, on a desperate, pleading note,

'Please let me come with you.' To her surprise Kent did not immediately answer and as she watched his changing expression her heart lifted and she was emboldened to say, 'I'd feel I was doing something to make up for my mistake. Do take me.'

The long and thoughtful silence ended with Kent's saying,

'Very well, Simoni—' He looked squarely at her. 'You know what it might mean?' She nodded, swallowing convulsively. Would she and Kent die together out there in that merciless desert? She said with a sort of swift agitation as if she would crush the idea of such a fatality, 'We'll be optimistic, as you said, and hope to find water.'

CHAPTER EIGHT

PREPARATIONS began immediately, with both Bill and Martin lending their assistance.

'We'll not cover more than two and a quarter miles an hour in this rough terrain,' observed Kent thoughtfully as he perused the map while the others busied themselves with the provisions which he and Simoni would take with them. For Kent, Simoni had improvised a rucksack from a seat-type parachute, cutting away the excess harness and the back pad. For herself she made a lighter pack from the canopy. Into these went their food and water, with the bulk of the space being taken up with water containers.

'You'd better wrap something round your ankles,' Kent recommended just before they were due to start. 'Strips of that parachute will do. Otherwise you're going to get sand in your shoes all the while.' He himself had on his boots, which would provide ample protection against the infiltration of sand.

At six o'clock, with an hour and a half of daylight left, Kent and Simoni set out for the wadi.

The night was clear, with a half-moon providing some light. But even so there was the usual lack of perspective always found in desert regions and Kent warned Simoni that what might appear to be a mere undulation in the landscape could prove to be a drop of forty or fifty feet.

When they had been travelling an hour he made a compulsory halt; this lasted ten minutes and was to be a regular occurrence. By half-past nine Kent estimated the distance covered to be about nine miles; they had a longer halt, partaking of a little food and a drink.

'It's good,' exclaimed Simoni, taking a drink. 'So very good!'

Kent nodded. 'It takes a situation like this to bring home to us the importance of water.' He watched her sip her drink slowly, savouring every single mouthful. 'It makes you vow you'll never again clean your teeth under a running tap,' he added with a hint of humour.

'It does,' she agreed fervently. 'Thinking of it now it seems criminal.'

Their meal finished they both bent over the map, Kent holding the torch. Their heads were close. It was an intimate and an unreal situation; two people alone in this hushed unfruitful world. No living thing in all the sterile distance, no sound but that of their own breathing. It was a situation fraught with drama and suspense as well, for even though there was an outward rejection of possible disaster, each was profoundly aware that there was a chance of their perishing together, here in this vast infecund wilderness.

'This is where we are at present.' Kent was pointing to a position on the map. 'The rate at which we've travelled means we're bang on schedule, so we're doing very nicely up till now. If we can keep this up we'll reach the wadi about eleven or just after, and should we be fortunate enough to find water within the hour then we should be leaving at about one o'clock, that's giving us an hour to fill the water cans and pack them in our rucksacks. If we do leave about one o'clock we should be back at camp before the sun is so high that travelling becomes really fatiguing.' He paused a moment and then, 'We'll take longer than we did coming because of the extra weight. And there *will* be some weight, Simoni. You're prepared for that?'

She nodded, then said, 'Supposing we don't find water within the hour?'

'Let's hope that if there is water, we shall find it without too much delay.' His tones had become grave and Simoni knew that the more time spent at the wadi the fewer hours of night would be left in which to make their return to camp. And should they have to walk under the searing heat of the sun they would soon weaken. Moreover, they would lose body water at the rate of over two pints an hour. . . .

Kent handed her the torch while he folded the map. The torch shook in her hand and he turned to her.

'What is it, Simoni?'

'I feel so blameworthy,' she quivered on a little husky note. 'Oh, Kent, how could I have been so utterly unthinking as to do a thing like that?'

'Forget it,' said Kent at once. 'The blame's not entirely yours. It's been a case of several circumstances combining to bring about the situation. Had my radio compass been working it wouldn't have mattered that you put your handbag on the dash. Had Martin not collapsed on to me I wouldn't have fluffed the landing – and had he not been taken ill at all a forced landing wouldn't have been necessary.' Kent stood up and Simoni did likewise. 'Don't think about it any more, Simoni; just keep up your strength and we'll win through.' His words brought a quivering smile to her lips and an immeasurable lightness to her heart.

'I'm glad you let me come,' she whispered, and fell

into step beside him, treading carefully because all the while she was terribly afraid of catching her foot on a boulder and twisting, or even breaking, her ankle. Such a disaster would not only ruin their chances of success but would naturally make Kent wish with all his heart that he had refused to listen to her plea that she should accompany him to the wadi.

'Are you tired?' Kent asked about an hour later when they made another ten-minute stop. Simoni shook her head. She was a little tired, but nothing would induce her to admit it at so critical a time as this.

'No, I'm fine for another twenty miles!'

He smiled faintly but made no comment, and they scarcely spoke at all during the last mile – the mile that should take them to the wadi, if nothing had gone wrong. At ten to eleven Simoni glanced at her watch and her heart gave a little jerk.

'Kent . . . we are on the right course?'

'Yes, I'm sure we are.' Looking back, he indicated the constellation of the Great Bear, which pointed to Polaris. 'There's the North Star. We're going this way – due south – which should bring us to the wadi. All right?'

She nodded, reassured, but said, 'Have we lost time, Kent?'

'No. The wadi should be appearing any time now.' And sure enough it did appear, and on reaching it they stood together looking down at the dry boulders and parched sand and silt of the river bed. With the rainy season not long since past both Kent and Simoni had wondered if they would be fortunate enough to find water in the wadi, although neither had mentioned it to the other. Obviously this had been a bad year for rain, for there was not even a sign of wet sand or mud in the narrow watercourse. Had there been any they would of course have utilized it, dipping cloths into it and wringing them out, and subsequently purifying the water to make it fit for consumption.

'Well,' decided Kent grimly, 'we'd better begin our search for a water hole. The stream bed's very narrow, so there's no point in working side by side. Nor is there anything to be gained by working upstream. So you can start here and work towards that boulder—' He pointed downstream. 'See it?' and when she nodded, 'I'll start at the boulder, so when you reach it you go on ahead and fix yourself another starting point. When I reach you I'll do the same.' Again Simoni nodded and Kent went on to say that undoubtedly any water holes would be known to the tribes of wandering bedouins, who invariably covered them with pieces of rock. 'It won't be easy to distinguish such a piece of rock in this light even with the aid of your torch. You'll have to keep a very careful look-out.'

They worked systematically, each searching a stretch of the watercourse and moving downstream as they did so.

Simoni's thirst was becoming unbearable when Kent called to her,

'Do you want a drink?'

'Can I? – oh, Kent, yes, please!' She moved towards him and they sat down on the bank. Kent doled out their rations.

'We're losing precious time,' he said after only five minutes, and they rose again, to begin the search once more. Barely ten minutes had passed when Simoni excitedly called his name, her voice ringing sharp and clear through the solemn deathlike silence of the barren void around her. Kent was stooping; she observed the dark smudge of his figure behind the probing shaft of light thrown off by his torch as he explored the silent river bed. On hearing her cry he straightened up and turned; at this distance she could detect no sign of emotion, but she did wonder if he were as strongly affected as she.

'I've found one! Kent – come quickly, I've found—' It was a moment of near hysteria, with Simoni waving her arms frantically, and her voice failing for a space because of the emotional disturbance blocking her throat. 'There's a water hole here. . . .'

A deep momentous silence followed and then Kent's torch was switched off. With a leap he was on the bank; this way his approach would be less difficult than that along the boulder-strewn river bed. Simoni never took her eyes off him. He looked tough, and totally remote. The amazing clarity of any desert atmosphere enlarges all objects, and it was a giant who strode towards her – while she herself felt small and somehow insignificant.

So long as water was found it did not matter who found it, yet Simoni was inordinately happy that it was she who had done so.

On reaching her Kent stood for a long moment gazing down at the great stone which she had managed to edge to one side, revealing the presence of the water hole underneath. The cover was heavy and she had left the complete removal of it to Kent. The silence was intense as they both stood there, side by side in this moon pale wilderness, remote from the busy world of men. To the west a few lonely hillocks rose above the almost featureless desert plain, while in the other direction a string of barchans, those crescentric dunes peculiar only to deserts, had coalesced to form a sinuous ridge above the smooth monotony of the tawny veneer.

Slowly Kent raised his eyes and looked into her face. She was still deeply affected by her emotions and knew she was on the verge of tears.

Unaware of this, Kent adopted an air of mock superiority, saying with the old quality of sarcasm,

'Do you realize, Load, that at last you've done something right? I always hoped the impossible might happen – and it has! My congratulations.' Because she could not see the laughing expression in his eyes Simoni's own filled up. Kent noticed this and now his severity became very real. 'Stop it! You can't afford to cry!' He shook her and she caught her lip between her teeth, biting hard on it as she fought to hold back the tears. Successful at last, she managed a smile and then Kent's arm was about her shoulders, his hand tightening on her elbow so that she felt its warmth through her anorak. It was a comradely gesture such as he might have extended to another man in circumstances as profound as these.

'Good girl,' he said. 'Ten out of ten for your powers of observation!'

They both laughed then, and with the tension dispelled Kent became brisk. He was in command again as he rapped out,

'Come, we're wasting precious time.' Bending down, he dragged away the stone covering the water hole. 'The lines? Are they in your pack, or mine?'

'I have them. . . .' She gave him one.

Attaching one of the containers to a line, he then lowered it into the hole, and a tense few seconds followed.

'It's very deep,' he frowned, letting out the line. It seemed an eternity before he murmured, 'Ah . . . !' and Simoni's eyes brightened and she gave a tinkling laugh of sheer joy. She was shining the lamp on the hole and her hand trembled as it had on a previous occasion.

'Water!' she breathed. 'Wonderful, marvellous – *blessed* water!'

Kent laughed, perhaps at her – or perhaps the increasing weight on the line was the sole reason for his lightheartedness.

'Here it comes, the first consignment.'

Staring at the container for a moment, both were too full to speak. The water, dark with moving particles of silt and fine rock debris, was impure at present . . . but it was life.

They both worked swiftly and methodically, Kent lowering one container while Simoni attached a line to another, having it ready when it was required. Kent's task took longer than hers and while she waited she crushed the halazone tablets, dropped them into the water and, securing the stopper, she gave each container a thorough shake. In an hour the water would be purified, and fit to drink.

With all the containers filled to capacity and the rock covering replaced over the water hole Kent took out his map and, using the hills and the string of barchans as pointers, marked on the map the position of the water hole.

'Might save someone else's life some time,' he said,

folding up the map again.

He allowed them a ten-minute break for a drink and a snack and then they were on their way again, their hearts light, undaunted by the long trek through the sandy wastes or by the immense weight on their backs, for they carried life itself. They were sure to be rescued before this supply of water ran out.

As usual they made a compulsory stop every hour and by four o'clock in the morning it became clear that their last few miles were going to give them some measure of discomfort.

'We lost time at the wadi.' Kent spoke matter-of-factly. They had been fortunate to find water and he had no grumble about the time it took. 'The sun will be heating up long before we make camp, I'm afraid.'

Simoni nodded; she felt fatigued but not excessively so, a circumstance for which she was grateful. She only prayed that her stamina would hold and that she would not be a burden on Kent, becoming so tired that their pace must be slackened.

Kent watched her as, unfastening her rucksack, she withdrew a packet of biscuits. Her anorak was dirty and so were her trews; her face was dust-begrimed and sticky with salt left by perspiration. She knew her eyes must be dull with tiredness and her hair felt as if it hadn't been washed for weeks. Kent was in no better condition; his face was grubby and so were his hands. He had black smudges under his eyes, and as she watched him she saw his lids droop once or twice and she became overwhelmed by a desire to put his head on her lap and let him sleep there, even though she ruefully admitted to herself that she would probably be the one to fall asleep first.

'What are you thinking?' His eyes had opened and he stared at her, curiously, and with an intentness that searched and probed – as on a couple of previous occasions his gaze had searched and probed.

'Nothing important,' she returned, but her flush gave evidence that her answer was not quite true.

'What?' he persisted, still fixing her gaze.

A shrug of her shoulders and then, 'You look tired,' she said, and he frowned at her.

'That's not an answer to my question.' His gaze was narrowed and faintly disturbing. She felt her colour heighten and to ease the moment she handed him the biscuits. He helped himself to a couple, but continued to stare at her, his head a little to one side, questioningly. With a little deprecating spread of her hands she said resignedly,

'I thought you – you needed somewhere to rest your head.' She glanced away then and reached for her beaker, handing it out hesitantly, requesting him by her action to give her her water ration. A faint smile touched his lips as, ignoring the beaker, he said, an odd inflection in his voice,

'And where, might I ask, would you consider a good place for me to rest it?'

Simoni glanced swiftly at him, remembering his taunting satire on previous occasions. A faint smile hovered on his lips and despite the tiredness still shadowing his eyes they held the merest hint of amusement. Was it possible that he read her thoughts? If so he was actually teasing her! Disconcerted and aware that he still awaited a reply which she was unable to give, Simoni moved her beaker, drawing his attention to it. He laughed softly, allowing his question to remain unanswered as, reaching for the water container which he had already taken from his pack, he uncorked it and doled her out some of the precious liquid.

'It's like nectar,' she breathed almost rapturously, even though the water had a distinct smell of chlorine, produced of course by the addition of the halazone tablets. 'We're safe now, aren't we?' she said then, confidence in her voice. 'I mean, even if by some mischance the rescue takes more time than we expect, we could go back to the wadi for more water.'

'We could, Simoni, but it's to be hoped the rescue will not be delayed too long. We haven't much food, for one thing, and so we should become considerably weakened. Also, I believe Martin has a more serious heart condition than he realizes, and Bill certainly requires medical attention.' He looked at her, shaking his head as he added gravely, 'No, it's to be hoped we shan't be compelled to go to the wadi again.'

With only two miles to go Kent suggested a longer rest than usual. He was reluctant to do this, but despite her determination not to flag Simoni was seriously affected by the weight on her back and by the temperature, for the sun had been up for some time and a pall of suffocating heat hung across the monotonous desert wastes. Her brain refused to function, her body was saturated, her legs leaden weights, and although she endeavoured to force herself harder, progress during the last mile had been excruciatingly slow. Some considerable way back Kent had taken two of her water cans despite her protest, and these he had carried in his hands.

They had reached a place where a moraine-like deposit of boulders – left there by flood waters in a bygone geological age when climatic conditions were far different from what they now were – afforded some shelter from the sun and that was the reason Kent decided to prolong their break.

'Let me do that.' Kent took Simoni's rucksack as she made to unfasten it with the intention of taking out the biscuits. She offered no resistance, but merely leant against a boulder and watched him. His face was grimed with sweat, particles of sand adhering to it. His hair was matted, even though she had seen him comb it several times, more to remove the sand than to improve its appearance. He turned to give her a shrewd look, examining her face and her hands, and then his eyes wandered right over her before coming back to her face.

'You look very tired.' His tone was gentle – not a tone she had ever heard him use before, either to her or anyone else. She suddenly hoped he would not be over-kind and sympathetic at this particular time, for as sure as she sat there she would burst into tears.

'I am tired.' Simoni managed a smile. 'But so are you.'

He ignored her second comment.

'Try to keep up. We'll probably take a long while to cover these last two miles, but we can then sleep for just as long as we like.' Bringing out the biscuits he handed her the packet. She shook her head.

'I couldn't, Kent—'

'Take a couple.'

Her mouth quivered. 'I'm not hungry.'

Using some of the paper wrapping to handle the biscuits, Kent extracted two from the packet and handed them to her.

'Be a good girl and do as you're told without a fuss.' Soft and moderately spoken words, but inflexible for all that. Listlessly she accepted them from him and forced herself to take a bite. He poured her a drink, which she received much more willingly, the ghost of a smile touching her lips.

'I'm sorry I'm like this—' A hand fluttered deprecatingly. 'I'll be all right again once I've rested.'

'I'd suggest going on and leaving you here,' he began, when she interrupted him.

'Oh, no, Kent – you mean, go on with your load and then come back for mine?' She shook her head emphatically. 'I wouldn't let you!'

His dark brows rose in censure. He said evenly,

'Were it possible for me to do so you wouldn't have any say in the matter. However, it isn't possible, for while at present this ridge provides us with shelter, it's so narrow that in about an hour – when the sun's higher – the shade will be reduced to a mere few inches. So I can't leave you.' He sat down, placing his beaker on the stone beside him. 'Eat your biscuits,' he ordered. 'And then you can relax for half an hour or so.'

'I mustn't go to sleep,' she murmured to herself a short while later. 'Whatever I do I must keep awake.'

'Simoni. . . .' The whisper being ineffective, Kent shook her gently. 'Simoni, it's time we were moving.'

She turned, blinked, then snuggled her head down and would promptly have gone to sleep again, but Kent gave her another little shake.

She opened her eyes, perception slowly dawning. And yet she did not move, but merely looked up, to see the glint of amusement in the tired eyes above her.

'You must have moved me . . . ?' Her lids drooped from sheer fatigue, and not owing to embarrassment. For there could be no embarrassment in this moment of intimacy and supreme isolation from the world.

'You looked as if you needed somewhere to rest your head,' he returned with a hint of satire, and although she did colour faintly then, she still remained where she was. To sleep was all she desired . . . to sleep in this most natural position, in the crook of Kent's arm, her head resting in that heavenly place between his shoulder and his breast. But her heaven was shattered by Kent's brisk,

'Come on. Move!'

'Yes.' She sighed deeply, making a half-hearted effort to lift her head. It fell back and she stared up into his face again, apologetically. A small silence descended on them as the intimacy returned. All that had gone before faded into insignificance. There never was a time when as her superior he had subjected her to cutting sarcasm or icy indifference; the incident at the Gulf Hotel was as nothing, nor was his inordinate power over her emotions. They were two people alone in the desert, having emerged triumphant from grave danger. It was still a moment of profound intimacy and, infected by it, Kent sought her lips, pressing a gentle kiss upon them. And when he lifted his head he smiled faintly because he knew the reason for her bewildered look was that his kiss had been soft and undemanding.

His lips touched hers again and despite her weariness a glow entered Simoni's eyes. Kent did not utter platitudes or pass trite remarks on her beauty – which in any case would not have been sincere, she thought with a rueful vision of her unkempt appearance. No, he merely said, looking down at her with a steadfast gaze,

'You've been a brick, Simoni.' This was what she would have him say in preference to a world of flattery, and happiness spread through her. 'I admit I had grave doubts about taking a woman on such a trek,' he was adding. 'And had either Bill or Martin been fit I'd never for a moment have contemplated taking you.' A small pause and a faint smile and then, 'But now, Simoni, I'd not hesitate to make the same decision again.' He eased her up; she left the support of his arm, putting a small distance between them.

'Thank you.' With her brain still befuddled by weariness she knew no caution and went on to state, 'You didn't kiss me this time because I resembled your fiancée.'

There was no stiffening on Kent's part, nor any other betrayal of resentment. Instead, he fell into a thoughtful silence. Simoni's own rather dazed mind reverted to Kent's request that she should take care of his friend's children. When on making the mistake which had resulted in such calamity, Simoni had concluded that that would be the end, that on their return to civilization Kent's one fervent hope would be that he would never set eyes on Simoni again as long as he lived. But this trek to the wadi had altered his opinion of her and she had no doubts at all that his offer still stood. Nor had she any doubts about her own decision. Never would she voluntarily say good-bye to Kent. Inevitably the time must come when she would be compelled to do so, but she had no intention of thinking about it. The near future made a pleasant picture, where she would live in the same house as Kent. What lay beyond that she refused to bring into focus.

'No,' Kent was suddenly saying, 'I didn't kiss you because you resembled Catherine.' At his words she thought about Ian and said on impulse,

'Your friendship with Ian – he stole your fiancée. . . .' She tailed off, very much afraid that she must surely have gone too far. But to her surprise Kent merely said, in an expressionless tone,

'No, Simoni, Ian did not steal my fiancée, as you put it.' And, surprising her still further, he went on to talk about Catherine, mentioning the other men she had when he was away. 'I was bound to discover this,' he added with a sort of grim reflection. 'And I naturally threw her over—' He broke off as he noted the rueful glance appearing in her eyes. 'I know what you're thinking about,' he told her with some amusement, 'But I assure you that was nothing to what Catherine had from me.'

Simoni gave a tiny shudder, but made no comment, and he went on to explain that although he and Ian had always been the best of friends they inevitably lost touch for long periods and it was during one of these that Kent became engaged to Catherine and so Ian never met her. In fact, he never knew Kent had been engaged. It was also during one of these periods, while Kent was based in Cyprus, that Ian, now in England, became engaged to Catherine, having met her, as Kent had previously done, in the Officers' Mess. She had attended a function as a guest, taken there by her father, who was also an officer in the R.A.F.

'Ian wrote and told me about his engagement, but made no mention of the girl's name – not that I would have suspected the girl was the same, even if he had. When next I happened to be in England he rang me, inviting me out to dinner with him and his fiancée so that I could meet her.' Kent paused a moment, a grim expression on his face. 'You can imagine what I felt like when I saw her. While Ian was busy with the wine waiter she begged me not to give her away, but I wasn't influenced in any way by that, and I pondered the matter over when I left them. However, I came to the conclusion that the way Ian felt about Catherine nothing I could say would make any difference. He would marry her. So the obvious course was to remain silent, which I did.'

'You made the wrong decision, it seems?'

He shrugged a trifle impatiently. 'As I've just said, my disclosure wouldn't have affected Ian's feelings for Catherine, and it would assuredly have affected our friendship. I just kept mum and hoped they'd be happy together.'

'They must have been happy at first,' Simoni put in thoughtfully after a while.

'They seemed all right until Vicki was about three. Then Ian was away a good deal and Catherine began going out, leaving the children with her mother – who in my opinion ought not to have assisted Catherine in this way. Catherine eventually met someone else and although Ian tried to stave off the break it was inevitable because Catherine was meeting this man whenever Ian was away from home.'

'Did you visit them – when Catherine was home?' Simoni asked curiously.

'I had to. Had I refused Ian would have wanted to know the reason. It was a damnable position for me, but I loved the children and they seemed to like me to visit them. Ian and I used to take them out for picnics sometimes.' His voice had become brisk and although he spoke of other things it was easy to see that his mind was now on the resumption of their journey. 'Come on, Simoni, up you get. Make one last effort and then you can sleep until we're rescued.'

Simoni asked him one final question as she rose to her feet.

'Kent . . . was it because I looked like Catherine that you didn't like me at first?'

'I certainly received a shock when I first saw you,' he admitted, but a frown knitted his brow as he added, 'I can't remember disliking you particularly.'

She looked searchingly at him and knew he spoke the truth. His initial dislike had existed only in her imagination, born of his complaints and reprimands when, unlucky as she was, things seemed always to be going wrong.

Kent was slinging his pack on his back; he then helped Simoni with hers, straightening out the straps and making her as comfortable as he could. He was above her and close, his hands on her shoulders while he manipulated the straps. Despite her distress and her utter exhaustion she was affected emotionally by the close proximity of him and turning swiftly she moved away, her colour heightening beneath the grime and sweat on her face.

Laughing, Kent took her chin in his hand and lifted it so that he could examine her more closely.

'You're not a bit like Catherine,' he declared, his laughter reflected in his eyes. 'Catherine never looked like this . . . and never could.' And, as she just had to be feminine all at once and display a little indignation, 'That was a compliment—' His hand moved to pat her cheek. 'And you know it, my girl, so you can take that injured look off your face!'

CHAPTER NINE

Two months had passed since the dramatic experience in the desert and Simoni had been employed by Kent for over six weeks, Kent having used some pull in order to obtain her release without her having to work a month's notice.

On their return, after having spent almost a week in the desert, all four had been taken to the hospital, Kent and Simoni being discharged after a couple of days. Bill and Martin had been kept in longer but they were all right now, although Martin had been warned to take care and he would be on tablets for the rest of his days.

Simoni's life had quickly assumed an orderly yet pleasant pattern. After breakfast on the sunlit patio with Kent and the children she would then take Catherine and Vicki to the beach, where they would often remain for the whole day, having their lunch in the *kafeneion* there. After tea Simoni would read to the children before putting them to bed. Kent would return from Nicosia and he and Simoni would dine together, chatting afterwards, or perhaps just reading in companionable silence. However, this routine would shortly change, for the schools would be opening the following week after the long summer break and Kent had arranged for the two little girls to attend the English school in Kyrenia. Already he had bought a small car for Simoni's use and one of her tasks would be to take the children to school and bring them back.

Kent was away from home for a couple of days every other week, being obliged to spend some time in his London office. But he preferred to be in Cyprus and had told Simoni he was training a man who would eventually be in charge of all the London business.

'I like to be where the sun is,' he told Simoni one evening when they were having a quiet drink on the terrace in the garden. But he smiled ruefully as he added, 'There's been only one occasion in my life when I didn't like the sun.'

Simoni nodded reflectively. 'I actually hated it. In fact, I wouldn't have cared if I'd never seen it again.'

'You might not have – had you failed to find that water.'

'It was nice doing something right for a change,' she returned, laughing, and a dart of amusement entered Kent's grey eyes.

'I'm thinking I must have been a most overbearing taskmaster in those R.A.F. days, Simoni.'

'You were,' she agreed, and there was no hesitation, because what had developed between Simoni and Kent since their shared danger could only be described as friendship, deep and sincere. Simoni, of course, would have wished something more emotional to enter into their relationship, but the gentle kiss Kent had given her in the desert had never been followed up by another. After six weeks living in the same house as Kent, Simoni believed she understood him fully. A confirmed bachelor, he had been all set for an affair with her on that night at the Gulf Hotel, especially at that moment which to him must undoubtedly have appeared to be a near surrender. However, the desert experience had strengthened his already growing respect for her and she knew that the idea of an affair was now dropped; and as there was no question of marriage, his friendship and regard for her would never develop into anything more emotional. Resigned, Simoni nevertheless often experienced difficulty in masking her own feelings, especially when Kent looked at her like this, or happened inadvertently to come a little close so that his nearness set her pulses racing, bringing back a vivid consciousness of his devastating power over her senses, a power she had discovered with that first kiss given her in the exotic scent-filled gardens of the Gulf Hotel.

'But now I've mellowed, it would appear.' Kent's soft rich voice cut into her musings and she glanced across at him and smiled.

'You've changed, yes.'

His eyes kindled as his amusement grew.

'So have you changed, my dear,' and the dryness in his tone was very marked as he went on to add, 'You're much braver now than you were.'

'But then I'm no longer in a subordinate position,' came the swift, intrepid rejoinder.

Kent gave a small laugh and changed the subject, asking after her family, for she had talked a good deal about her parents, and about her brother and sister.

'I had another letter from Cindy this morning,' she informed him, adding, 'She's home from Canada, as I mentioned. Mother's delighted because Cindy has decided not to roam again for a while. We've all travelled and Mum hasn't enjoyed us as much as most mums enjoy their children.'

A small silence followed and then Kent said,

'If you want to ask your family over for a holiday, Simoni, do so by all means. We'll manage to fix them up somehow, by a little re-shuffling.'

Simoni's eyes glowed; she told him that Cindy had suggested that she come over but that she, Simoni, had written back evasively because she hadn't liked to ask Kent if her sister could stay at the villa.

'My parents won't come,' she added, 'because they're expecting my brother home next month, but Cindy will jump at the invitation. Thank you, Kent, for offering to have her here.'

'Don't thank me, Simoni; I'm the one who should be grateful. You've made a big sacrifice in agreeing to throw up your job and look after Catherine and Vicki. I appreciate what you've done and I'm only too happy to be able to repay you in some small way.'

Her heart gave a little jerk. If only he knew how this quiet intimate moment upset her equilibrium! To her relief Kent did not appear to expect any comment from Simoni as, picking up his glass from the table, he teetered back on his chair, stretching out his legs before him. In the softly subdued illumination from the lamps half hidden in the trellised vines shading the terrace his face took on a sort of unassailable dignity which was no less formidable than the granite-like countenance so familiar to Simoni in the old days when Captain Kent Travers was her stern exacting boss. A soft breeze suddenly set the vine leaves trembling; Kent's features changed with the play of light, miraculously taking on a soft and almost gentle aspect, and Simoni had ruthlessly to crush a rising access of yearning and excitement.

On the breeze was wafted the tantalizing pervasive

scent of myrtle, in ancient times a symbol of peace and happy marriage, and sacred to Aphrodite, pagan goddess of beauty and love. On the breeze also drifted the night sounds – cicadas in the nearby olive trees and goat bells on the mountainside, the sad and futile cry of a donkey tethered to the bare brown earth, the distant haunting strains of *bouzouki* music echoing from a spangle of lights where a village lay cradled amid the towering purple splendour of the Kyrenia massif.

Aware of the piercing concentration of her companion's gaze, Simoni turned her head and their eyes met. She swallowed the accumulation of saliva on her tongue; the action seemed to bring a strange little ache to the side of her throat. Kent watched, his slender brown fingers negligently twisting the stem of his glass. Slowly he came forward until the front legs of the chair grounded with a vibrating little crash on the mosaic floor of the terrace. He put down his glass and Simoni looked away and swallowed again. He was going to rise and come close, he would kiss her. . . .

The night was too enchanting, too hushed and still . . . too tempting by far, and with an abruptness which clearly took Kent by surprise Simoni stood up, announcing her intention of going to bed.

'Now?' Automatically Kent glanced at his watch. 'It's only half past nine!'

She nodded and moved, placing her chair closer to the table.

'I'm rather tired.' Lame and unconvincing words, but Simoni could think of nothing else to say.

'Tired? The children?' He sounded anxious, she thought and swiftly shook her head. Kent went on before she could speak, 'They'll be at school in a couple of days, so you can have a rest.' She stood gazing down, overwhelmingly conscious of his magnetism.

'It isn't the children,' she murmured, picking up the book lying on a nearby chair. 'I just want to – to relax in bed and – and read.'

So strangely he regarded her, from under frowning brows, puzzled by her manner, and by her decision to retire so early. But to her relief he made no attempt to dissuade her and with a forced little smile she bade him good night and made her escape.

But on entering her room she was restless and instead of getting undressed she moved to the window and stepped out on to the balcony. To her surprise Kent was there below. She saw his shadowed frame against the fragrant hedge of oleanders.

He walked slowly, and with an air of preoccupation about him from which Simoni gained the impression that he too was restless. She frowned, and fell into a mood of reflective thought. There had been several occasions recently when she had sensed his restlessness, and she knew instinctively that there were times when he was a very different man from the confident, superior Kent Travers she had known in the old days. Another odd circumstance was the occasional abrupt change in his manner towards her – from attentive charm one moment to cool disinterest the next. This dramatic switch seemed to indicate a sudden realization on Kent's part that he was carrying his new friendship with Simoni too far, that he was unbending just a little too much, and so he would pull himself up with a jerk, endeavouring to erase any impression of over-indulgence he had given. Following immediately on one of these abrupt changes would be Kent's rather stiff assertion that he had work to do, and he would instantly leave her and she would not see him for the rest of the evening.

The following morning she and Kent took Catherine and Vicki on to the beach. There were more people than usual for, it being Sunday, the businessmen from Nicosia had flocked into Kyrenia, bringing their wives and families for a day at the seaside. This was a regular occurrence and, watching one particular family – father, mother and three sturdy boys, all in the water – Simoni turned to Kent, who lay on the sands beside her, his eyes never wavering from the two little ones in the water, Catherine a few yards out and Vicki close to the shore.

'It's always a matter of wonderment to me how the natives of this island can be so different – I mean, the people living in Nicosia are so modern in outlook, and yet in that village up there—' She broke off, pointing into the mountains behind the shore, '—those people are so backward.'

'You mean that the women are different.' He smiled in some amusement and added before she could speak, 'I agree with you, Simoni. Wives of Nicosia businessmen are no different from those of the West, while the village wives are totally unemancipated. It's odd, because the distance between Nicosia and that village up there can't be more than fifteen miles.'

'I wonder if the village women envy those from Nicosia.'

Kent shook his head, his eyes still on the children.

'They seem happy enough – they're always ready with a smile, if that's anything to go by.'

This was true. Cypriots, whether men or women,

whether Greek or Turkish, were always smiling and content. Perhaps it was the sunshine, thought Simoni. For there were fewer than twenty days a year on which the sun did not shine. Even during the 'rainy season' from November to March, the downpours were invariably followed by brilliant warm sunshine. During her years in the Air Force Simoni had flown to the island many times and consequently she knew what it was like at all times of the year.

Kent was calling to Catherine and Vicki; they came to him at once and he attended to Vicki while Simoni saw to Catherine. Simoni watched him covertly as, after Vicki had discarded her brief covering Kent wrapped her in a towel and rubbed her down. Something profoundly disturbing affected Simoni, as well it might, under the circumstances, her feelings for Kent being what they were. Kent as a father. . . . Would he help with his own children like this? His own? Would he ever marry? Simoni wondered, her thoughts suddenly going to Thora Benson, yet just as suddenly Simoni put the image from her. On the couple of occasions when, shopping in Nicosia, Simoni had called into the office with the children, Thora had been there, with Kent – just the two of them in his private office. . . . And on the times when Thora came to the villa she acted in such a proprietorial way that she might almost be expecting some day to be the mistress there although she never acted so before Kent, Simoni had noticed, and could not help wondering how he would react if she had.

'There – all dressed and pretty!'

Kent turned to Simoni. 'Have you a comb?'

'In my bag.' She was towelling Catherine and

merely indicated the brightly-coloured beach bag lying on the sand. The next moment Kent was combing Vicki's hair.

'Keep still, you rascal!' Kent was standing up now, a giant above the laughing tiny tot whose saturated curls he was endeavouring to put into place. Suddenly aware of Simoni's concentrated gaze, he slowly turned his head, a hint of amusement in his eyes. Simoni flushed a little, then smiled; Kent responded and said, the merest hint of satire in his tone, 'Why so surprised, Simoni?'

Her lashes fluttered down. She said, reaching for Catherine's dress and preparing to put it over her head,

'I don't know what you mean.'

Her evasion served to increase his amusement.

'I've astounded you by turning out to be human.'

She laughed then and told Catherine to turn around. The buttons of her dress fastened, Catherine escaped with a swift mischievous turn and would have run off without having her hair combed, but her hand was caught in Kent's and she was brought to a halt, laughing up at him. Nice to be a child, thought Simoni. You had no embarrassing thoughts about men like Kent, and about their devastating masculinity.

After lunch they all took a siesta, for the intense heat of July and August had continued into September. At four in the afternoon all came to life again and Simoni glanced down from her bedroom window to see Kent and the two children in the garden playing ball. What patience he had! And how *impatient* he'd been with Simoni in those days when his position gave him authority over her. Never did she surmise then that she would feel like this about him!

Sensing her attention, he glanced up. She smiled and he responded. Stupid to encourage that smile. Simoni frowned to herself. How could a smile send a spasm of sheer ecstasy through her like this?

'*Kopiaste!*' he called, and she laughed. Come and join them. . . .

'I'll come and join you in a few minutes. I want to wash my hair.'

'Your hair looks lovely, Auntie Sim,' called up Vicki, using the diminutive of her name of which Kent definitely did not approve. 'Come on – *kopiaste!*'

'All right.' She went down the steps and ruffled Vicki's hair as she reached her. 'Swanking with our Greek, aren't we?'

'That's all she knows,' put in Catherine, running to catch the ball Kent had thrown to her. 'I know a lot more than Vicki does. But of course she's only young,' added Catherine as her sister's face took on a pout. 'She's only five and I'm six—'

'Not again, Catherine,' interrupted Kent, negligently stretching out a hand to catch the ball Catherine had returned to him. 'Vicki doesn't want to be reminded all the time that she's younger than you are.'

After tea Simoni read to the children for a while and during this time Kent was in his study. But from dinner time onwards Simoni would have his companionship and always she looked forward to these pleasant interludes.

'Have you phoned the hospital today?' she asked when after dinner they followed their normal routine and took their coffee on the patio.

'I rang just after tea.' Kent stopped and sighed and became grave. 'He's still hanging on to life by a thread.'

'There's no improvement at all?'

Kent shook his head. 'Frankly, I don't believe he wants to live.'

Simoni caught her breath, distressed and hurt, somehow.

'That a young man should want to die—' She made a negative gesture with her hand. 'No, I can't agree with you, Kent. He has the children, even if he's lost his wife.'

'It's because he's lost his wife that he has no will to live.' Kent spoke now on a decisive note as if he no longer had any doubts that Ian wanted to die. 'Catherine certainly affected him more deeply than she affected me.'

Simoni glanced up swiftly. This was Kent in a soft communicative mood, a mood she loved and always wished to prolong. It savoured of intimacy, the sort of intimacy for which she yearned and which she knew would never become a permanent state between her and the man who in the past had regarded her with such disdain and had once told her brutally that she was the most incompetent A.L.M. with whom he had ever worked.

'Ian was married to her, though.' Simoni spoke at last, half to herself, because she was wondering how any girl, having been lucky enough to attract a man like Kent, could risk losing him by flirting with other men. Had she, Simoni, been so lucky she would have found fulfilment in just waiting, waiting for the heavenly interludes when Kent returned to base, and during the waiting she would dream . . . dream of the reunion and the lovemaking and the future when they were married. A tiny sigh of dejection left her lips, rising above the nocturnal grating sound of the cicadas in the olive trees, and Kent looked across at her, his face appearing stern and set owing to the shadows cast by the lamps half hidden among the trellised vines.

'Why the sigh?' he inquired, amusement in his tone.

Delicate colour fused her face; her fingers resting on the table moved a little, in a sort of nervous gesture. How disconcerted he would be were she to voice the reason for that sigh!

'It was an unconscious thing,' came the careless response. 'One sighs for nothing sometimes.'

His gaze was fixed upon her, faintly narrowed as if by this he could the more closely examine her.

Something indefinable in his manner puzzled her for a space and then there flashed through her mind a possibility that brought a gasp to her lips. Could Kent, by some miracle, be affected by her just as she was by him? It seemed incredible and yet it would explain those variations of mood which had so perplexed her. If Kent were beginning to care, though, he was obviously not being drawn into anything so restrictive and permanent as marriage; hence his swift protective move whenever he found himself off guard. Had she possessed sufficient experience and guile Simoni did not doubt that she could without too much difficulty have penetrated the formidable armour, but, unequipped as she was, she could only remain helplessly inactive, dismally aware that the interlude of stalemate afforded Kent more time in which to strengthen the defence which he apparently intended at all costs to sustain.

Reflecting first on the general opinion at the station that Kent was a confirmed bachelor, and then thinking of his ex-fiancée, Simoni reached the conclusion that his experience with Catherine had resulted in his having made up his mind never to fall in love again.

'It was an unconscious thing, was it?' Kent broke the silence at last, murmuring the words almost to himself. 'One usually has a reason for sighing.' Still his voice murmured. He was no longer looking at her, but at a giant moth that had settled on the table and was fluttering its wings. What was he thinking? she wondered, her own eyes moving to the sea and to the moon's white path which quivered towards the shore.

She sighed again, but this time she smiled too and said,

'I love these balmy nights, with the moon and stars, and the sounds and smells.'

'So do I. You know you're in the East on a night like this.' His gaze lifted and wandered to the moon hanging over the sea, but he made no further comment.

'I love the East,' breathed Simoni, reaching for her coffee cup.

Turning, he looked at her. 'If Ian doesn't recover you'll stay?' He spoke with confidence and she nodded.

'Yes, Kent, I'll stay.'

But how, she wondered, would she continue indefinitely to hide her feelings for him?

Cindy arrived a fortnight later, and as Catherine and Vicki had started school Simoni was able to give her sister a good deal of her time. Kent seemed quite taken with Cindy and she with Kent. But then Cindy was full of life, always cheerful and optimistic no matter what the circumstances.

'Never meet trouble half-way,' she immediately advised Kent when, one evening, the conversation turned to Ian and his children. 'A father isn't deliberately going to die and leave two babes like those. Why, they're adorable! I thought my three were the most wonderful kids in the world, but those two are just about the cutest I've ever seen.'

Kent smiled. 'By "your three" I presume you mean the children you were caring for in Canada?'

A broad grin crossed Cindy's pretty face and was reflected in her large blue eyes.

'That's right – although I might as well tell you I wouldn't have minded if they'd been mine.'

'It seems to me,' mused Kent, glancing from one sister to the other, 'that you're both born mothers.'

'We always loved babies as children.' Cindy looked at Simoni and laughed. 'Do you remember how we used to take everyone's babies out? – and, later, how we'd baby-sit every night in the week?'

Simoni nodded and added reminiscently, 'We said we were going to have six apiece, remember?'

'Sure – and I still intend having six – when I can find a man, that is,' Cindy added twinklingly, and Kent, having listened with amused interest to the sisterly interchange, joined in to say he was quite sure Cindy would have no difficulty in finding a man willing to marry her.

'You must have had many offers,' he said, but for some reason his eyes strayed to Simoni.

'I have,' Cindy agreed without any attempt at mod-

164

esty. 'But they all leave me cold.' With a mock despairing gesture she spread her hands. 'It isn't that I want perfection, but somehow I just can't find a suitable mate!'

They all laughed at her way of putting it and Kent said,

'There's a lucky man somewhere – all unsuspecting of the good fortune in store for him.'

It was customary for Kent to take the children to see their father every Tuesday. This having been explained to their teacher, they were not expected in school on Tuesday afternoons. When the day for their visit came round Kent, much to Simoni's surprise, suggested that she and Cindy go to the hospital with him and the two little girls.

'Ian has no visitors other than the children and myself,' he went on to add for Cindy's benefit. 'I think it might be good for him to meet someone new.'

Simoni understood what he meant. New faces might help to jerk Ian from the apathy into which he had fallen.

'Of course we'll come,' responded Cindy eagerly. 'The poor man – he wants cheering up.'

Ian was in a private ward and all five entered together. He lay back against the pillow, his face pale and drawn and almost devoid of flesh. It still remained unmoving even when the children, running to the bed, cried in unison,

'Hello, Daddy!'

'Hello.' His tone was flat; Kent and Simoni exchanged glances, both deeply affected by Ian's lack of interest in his children.

'We've brought you some more visitors,' Catherine

said, leaning across the bed and rising on tiptoe to give her father a loud kiss. 'Auntie Sim – you know all about her – and Auntie Cindy. They're sisters, just like Vicki and me.'

Ian's eyes moved then to regard the girl who came slowly towards the bed. Watching her, Simoni saw the compassion in her lovely eyes, and the faint tremor of her lips.

'Meet Cindy.' Kent's voice was soft; he too was intently watching Cindy's face.

'Nice to meet you, Ian.' For once Cindy's brisk and cheerful manner had deserted her. Mechanically she took the chair Kent had brought forward for her. She touched the fleshless hand lying on the cover and repeated, a distinct catch in her voice, 'Nice to meet you, Ian.'

CHAPTER TEN

A RUEFUL smile came to Simoni's lips as she read her mother's letter, and Kent, having picked up his brief-case, raised a questioning brow and stood waiting for her to speak.

'Mum bemoans the fact of Cindy's having deserted her once more.'

'She wants her home, you mean?'

'Not really. Mum's quite resigned to the fact that her children roam.'

A moment's silence followed and then,

'If you explain to your mother about the miracle Cindy's wrought she won't mind her daughter being away from home, I'm sure.' With a smile Kent left her and she walked out on to the patio and watched his car roll smoothly along the drive and then become lost in a cloud of ochre-coloured dust as it travelled the unmade lane leading down to the main road.

Miracle? Yes, indeed it was a miracle . . . but what was to be the outcome for Cindy? Simoni shook her head and sighed. She had not yet questioned her sister about her feelings for Ian, having until quite recently concluded that it was no more than compassion that drew Cindy to the hospital on every single visiting day. Cindy's stay in Cyprus, which was originally for a fort-night only, was now entering its fifth week and she still made no mention of leaving. Not that Simoni wanted her to leave, just the contrary. Nor did Kent want her to leave; this he had emphatically declared to Simoni one evening last week when, after dinner, they found themselves alone for a few minutes, Cindy having gone to her room to write letters.

'I firmly believe, Simoni, that Ian owes his life to Cindy.'

Simoni nodded reflectively. 'He rallied from the first moment of seeing her.'

These musings were interrupted as Cindy and the children came through the sitting-room to join Simoni on the patio.

'Auntie Sim, isn't it an exciting day!' Catherine and Vicki both had tiny satchels slung over their backs and spotless white hankies peeping from their pockets. Their hair was shining and plaited and tied with wide pink ribbons. Cindy had taken over quite early and when Simoni told Kent she was not now earning her money he said, an odd inflection in his voice,

'Let Cindy do it; she's obviously enjoying herself.'

'Because of Daddy?' Simoni smiled down at the eager little upturned face. 'Yes, Catherine, it is an exciting day.'

'He's coming to live here for a bit, isn't he, Auntie Sim?' Vicki slipped a small hand into that of Simoni, then pressed her cheek against it. 'It'll be lovely having our daddy with us again!'

No mention of their mother now, thought Simoni, wondering how Catherine could have left them, neither knowing nor caring what was happening to them. Had it not been for Kent they would have been flown to England, to Ian's sister, where with the passing of time they would have forgotten their father just as quickly as they had forgotten their mother.

'I don't really want to go to school,' said Catherine,

glancing a little expectantly up at Cindy.

'Daddy isn't coming home until this afternoon.'

'I can't wait!' Catherine gave a big sigh, and then, 'Uncle Kent said Daddy can't play with us yet, and we mustn't worry him too much because he isn't properly better.'

'No, darling, he isn't,' said Simoni. 'But when he's had a good long rest he'll be able to play with you again.'

'That'll be lovely!' Vicki jumped up and down and then added, 'All of us? We'll all go on the sands and play together?'

Simoni nodded, swallowing unconsciously. Her time on the island was now running out, for very soon Ian would be making his own arrangements regarding his children, and Simoni would then leave the island to take up the post Kent had promised to find for her.

Cindy accompanied her to the school, and having dropped the children Simoni parked the car near the market.

After traversing narrow alleyways flanked by tall sandy-coloured houses from whose rusty iron balconies exotic flowers spilled incongruously from petrol cans and worn-out buckets, the two girls reached the harbour and sat down at an umbrella-shaded table on the waterfront. Dominating the quaint, picturesque harbour, with its bright array of pleasure craft, was the massive Lusignan castle built in the thirteenth century on the site of an earlier Byzantine fortress which fell to the gallant Crusader, Richard the Lionheart, when, driven on to the island by storms, and given a most hostile reception by the Byzantine Emperor, Isaac Comnenos, Richard decided to conquer the island. Imploring Richard not to fetter him in irons, Isaac was fettered in chains of silver.

'This is a fantastic island!' Cindy leant back in her chair, her eyes moving from the backcloth of tall Venetian houses to the brightly-coloured boats bobbing about in the water. 'How I'd love to settle here!'

'Is there any possibility of your doing so?' asked Simoni, her meaning quite clear to her sister.

'I don't know for sure.' Cindy fell silent a moment and then, 'I'd love to take care of those two children for Ian,' she murmured. 'He feels certain his wife will never come back to him.'

'Would he have her if she did?'

A frown came swiftly to Cindy's brow. 'I rather believe he would,' she said at last on a little trembling sigh.

'He'd think of the children, you mean?'

'That's one reason, I suppose—' Cindy broke off, and her frown deepened. 'I believe he's still in love with his wife.'

'How strange.' Simoni shook her head and fell silent in thought. And then, without thinking, 'Some women have all the luck and don't appreciate it. Catherine's had two marvellous men and played around with them both.'

'Two?' echoed Cindy, and a flush rose to Simoni's cheeks.

'She was engaged to Kent once,' she replied after a small hesitation, and her sister gasped.

'Kent! Then why is he so good to Ian?'

'Ian didn't take Catherine from Kent.' Simoni stopped speaking as the waiter approached with his tray. Having been served with their drinks, she went on to repeat all Kent had told her. 'Kent feels guilty about it, but as he said there was really nothing he could do because Ian was so in love with Catherine that he would never have given her up.'

'So Catherine's been no good right from the start, it appears.' Simoni made no comment and Cindy went on, in a somewhat dreamy tone, 'I expect she must have been very beautiful to attract two men like Ian and Kent.'

A rather wry smile came to Simoni's lips and hovered there a moment.

'I have a look of her,' she said presently, and Cindy flashed her an interrogative glance.

'What do you mean?'

'I resemble her. Take a look in Catherine's locket some time—' Simoni broke off, frowning. 'I haven't seen that locket lately,' she then went on, her frown deepening.

'I've never seen a locket at all.'

'I hope she hasn't lost it. Kent bought it for her.'

Picking up her glass, Cindy took a long cooling drink, then placed the glass back on the table.

'Does Catherine really look like you?'

'We are very alike, yes.' Simoni paused a moment and then, 'When Kent was my boss I used to think he didn't like me because I looked like her.'

'Didn't Kent like you?' queried Cindy, an odd inflection in her voice.

'I felt he didn't, but I don't now believe he really disliked me. He was just indifferent most of the time and mad with me some of the time.'

'Why so?'

Simoni shrugged and gave a deprecating laugh.

'I was often in trouble with him. Kent's a stickler for efficiency and all sorts of things went wrong when first I worked with him. I seemed to be dogged by bad luck – true, some of the mishaps could be placed at my door,' she swiftly owned, 'but others could not. However, Kent would blow me up whether the blame were mine or not, and that was the reason I gained the impression he disliked me.'

Cindy looked at her in silence for a while and then,

'Kent certainly doesn't dislike you now,' she asserted in quiet tones of conviction.

'No; in fact, we're very good friends.' Friends. . . . A little ache of dejection swept over Simoni. Almost six weeks had passed since that moment of enlightenment when she had become convinced that Kent was not quite so heartwhole as she had believed, nor as he himself would have wished, and yet they were still only friends, with not the merest hint of affection creeping into Kent's attitude towards her.

A fortnight after Ian came out of hospital Simoni found herself alone with Kent. They were on the beach, Ian and Cindy having taken Kent's car and gone into Kyrenia to get the children some shoes. Kent had just come out of the water and was standing there, towelling himself. Simoni lay on the warm sand, her hands behind her head, looking out towards the hazy horizon. It was now the middle of October, but the sun shone from a clear sky and it was still quite warm enough for bathing.

'Ian was talking about going home.' Simoni spoke casually, but her nerves were tensed as she went on, 'That job you promised to get for me – I shall be leaving the island soon.'

Kent threw down the towel and sat on it, silent for a while, his gaze, like hers, fixed on the indistinct line dividing sea and sky.

'I'll see to it on Monday,' he promised at length.

'Thank you.' Simoni swallowed hard and turned her head to one side, unwilling to let him see the quick defensive fluttering of her lashes. Tears. ... Rarely did she cry, but at this moment the tears were very close. Somehow, during these past two weeks when they had all been so happy together there had been a growing hope on Simoni's part for a reprieve, although she had no clear picture of the form this reprieve would take.

'I believe,' said Kent after a while, 'that there's every possibility of Ian's asking Cindy to stay on and become a sort of nanny-housekeeper for him.'

Simoni nodded. Neither Cindy nor Ian had mentioned anything of the kind, but the most natural thing was for him to ask Cindy to go and work for him.

'Cindy will like that.'

Kent hesitated and then turning to her,

'They get on very well together.'

Simoni's head came round; she sat up and drew her knees under her chin, embracing them with her arms.

'Cindy thinks Ian will take his wife back if she should return.' Simoni spoke her thoughts aloud, then realized they were not exactly relevant.

'I'm not so sure about that.'

'He'd think of the children.'

'That's natural, I suppose.' Kent became thoughtful.

'Unless she returns very soon, though, I honestly don't think she'll have a chance.'

'No?' Simoni spoke breathlessly. 'He'll fall in love with Cindy?'

'He's half way there, in my opinion.'

'There would have to be a divorce.'

A half-sneer of contempt marred the attractive form of his mouth.

'That won't be difficult.'

'Mother would hate the idea of Cindy's marrying a divorced man with two children,' said Simoni, again voicing her thoughts aloud.

'At first, perhaps, but she'd change her mind once she'd seen Ian.'

Simoni nodded in agreement. 'He's nice.' She paused and then, smiling in recollection, 'Dad wouldn't mind. He's always saying he wants to be a grandfather.'

Kent said nothing and the atmosphere became strained; nervously Simoni dug her fingers into the sand, picking up a handful and letting it trickle through her fingers. Repeatedly she did this and suddenly her fingers touched something hard and a second later she was holding Catherine's gold locket in the palm of her hand.

'Where did you get that?' Kent stared at it in amazement. 'You said it was lost—'

'How lucky!' Simoni broke in, quite unable to believe her eyes. True, they always came to the same spot on the beach, but it was still a million to one chance that the locket should have come to light. 'I've found it in the sand. It's incredible!'

'Catherine seemed to think she'd lost it at school.'

Taking the locket from Simoni as he spoke, Kent snapped it open and stared at the lovely face looking back at him. Casting him a glance from under her lashes, Simoni saw the tightening of his mouth, the steely coldness of his eyes producing the impression of harshness amounting almost to cruelty. It was only the second occasion on which Simoni had noticed this harshness and for some reason it sent a tingle down her spine. She thought she knew him by now, for she had seen him in many moods, had seen him stern and authoritative, and insufferably sarcastic; she had seen him in the changing mood of interest and indifference, or hardness and deep compassion ... but now she sensed an altogether different mood and knew instinctively that he could be totally without mercy. Simoni hoped that she herself would never provoke him into that particular mood.

With a snap the locket was pressed shut and at that moment Catherine and Vicki came flying across the sand, followed by Ian and Cindy. Expecting Kent to give Catherine her locket Simoni was surprised to see his hand close on it.

'Uncle Kent! We've got some lovely new shoes, and a dress each – that lady makes them in the shop in Catsellis Street! She does them on a sewing machine – not in the shop, but in another room. Isn't she clever?'

'She is indeed. Where are the dresses?'

'In the car. We've left the car under the vines, like you always do, Uncle Kent!' Catherine chattered on and on until, laughing, Cindy interrupted with,

'Darling, it's time you stopped for breath.'

'Yes – but I like talking.'

'So do I like talking.' Vicky sat down on Kent's knee and, noticing his closed fist, began to dig in her fingers saying, 'What have you got, Uncle Kent?'

'It's nothing for little girls—'

'I want to see it!'

'I do as well.' Catherine flopped down on Kent's other knee. 'Let me see – oh, *please*!'

Curiously Simoni watched him, her wonderment increasing when it became plain that Catherine was not to have her locket.

Catherine pouted at failing to get her own way, but almost immediately forgot about Kent's closed fist and began to chatter incessantly. Ian this time told her it was time she stopped for breath.

'I know it is,' Catherine agreed readily, but grinned mischievously, repeating, 'I like talking, though!' Her father laughed. How well he looked, thought Simoni, well and healthy and quickly acquiring a tan. Cindy turned to him as she herself laughed; her face was flushed, her eyes aglow with an unusual brightness.

'It's tea time,' said Kent, rising and picking up his towel as he did so.

'You don't want a lift,' said Ian. 'You came in Simoni's car, I noticed.' Kent merely nodded, but to Simoni's surprise Kent did not follow when Ian and Cindy strolled towards the parking space, the two little girls racing on ahead.

'Aren't we going yet?' Simoni stood there, puzzled. Kent nodded absently, and before she guessed his intention there was a wide swing of his arm; the locket whizzed through the air, glinting against the sunlight before it dropped, sending up a tiny spout of water as it hit the sea.

Simoni stared; the action was so unfathomable, and so unlike anything she would have expected from Kent.

'Why did you do that?' she asked, and he turned to her.

'Didn't you see the expression on their faces?' he inquired, and Simoni shook her head, more bewildered than ever.

'The children's faces—?'

'On the faces of Ian and Cindy.'

Her eyes widened. She recalled Cindy's flushed cheeks and shining eyes.

'You mean—?'

'What was in that locket was not what Cindy would want to be conscious of all the time. And as the photograph couldn't go without the locket they've both gone. Give me a reminder on Monday morning when I go out. I'll get Catherine a replacement in Nicosia.'

Kent proved to be right about Ian and Cindy. At dinner that evening Ian told Simoni and Kent that he was intending to divorce Catherine as soon as possible and marry Cindy.

'I'm very glad for you both.' Kent spoke softly and his grey eyes strayed to Simoni. It was a sort of compulsive act and Kent instantly glanced away again.

Looking from her sister to Ian, Simoni murmured, echoing Kent's words with deep sincerity,

'I'm so glad for you both. I'm sure you're going to be very happy.'

'Cindy's coming to housekeep for me – while we're waiting, that is,' Ian told his listeners eagerly. 'I'm hoping the waiting won't be too long,' he added, darting a tender glance in Cindy's direction.

As Kent went out on the following Monday morning Simoni reminded him about Catherine's locket.

'And, Kent. . . .'

'Yes?' He was already on his way out, but he turned and it seemed to Simoni that the abruptness of his movement denoted impatience.

'You'll see about my job?'

He nodded. 'Yes, I haven't forgotten, Simoni. I'll make sure you have as good a post as you gave up – or an even better one.' He smiled at her and left.

She took the children to school and by the time she came back Cindy and Ian had gone out. For several days Ian had been accompanying Kent to the office in Nicosia, for he would be grounded for a while and Kent was handing over some of the work to him temporarily. But today he and Cindy were going to Ian's house to open it up and do some straightening up, for at the time of the accident Kent had instructed Thora to see that dust covers were put on everything. Ian's car was in the garage at his house. He would be picking that up and he and Cindy would come back to the villa in it. Cindy had written to her mother the previous night, telling her of what had transpired and saying she would be settling permanently in Cyprus. Simoni now sat down and wrote to her mother, informing her that she would be returning to England in the very near future. The letter finished, Simoni went into the village to post it. Brown-skinned men sat outside the *kafeneion*, which was also the post office and the village store and the centre from which all the villagers bought their butane gas cylinders.

That night, restless and unhappy at the idea of

leaving the island, and leaving Kent, Simoni excused herself and went to bed early. Cindy and Ian walked in the garden and then Cindy also came upstairs. She called good night as she passed Simoni's door and Simoni answered in tones of forced lightness. After about half an hour she got up and, without putting on the light, stepped out on to her balcony. The night was balmy and scented and a soft warm breeze caressed her hair and tousled it. She sat down on a chair and became lost in thought. The future, which had seemed so rosy when on leaving the Air Force she had begun working with Bill, now looked dark and drear, with not a ray of light anywhere.

She had been foolish and now she must pay. She should have known Kent was not for her . . . and yet she could not forget his gentleness and the comradeship that had sprung up between them in the face of danger, out there in the endless desert. She'd been a brick, Kent had said, and at that time it was the sort of compliment she preferred to any other, but now. . . . At last she rose with the intention of returning to bed, when suddenly she heard voices. Kent and Ian in the garden – discussing her! Simoni went hot all over and sat down weakly as she heard,

'She loves you, Kent, anyone can see that.'

'More fool her!'

'The way she looks at you – making no effort to hide it—'

'I know. It's a damned nuisance! What's wrong with women that they fall in love so easily?' Kent spoke impatiently, angrily almost, and Ian gave a soft, humorous laugh.

'You shouldn't be so attractive—'

'This is no time for joking,' Kent cut in shortly. 'I'm concerned only with the inconvenience.'

'But she's going shortly.' Ian returned soothingly, though still amused, judging by his tones. The men were walking on and their voices became fainter and fainter despite the clarity of the atmosphere. 'You'll be all right in a couple of weeks' time. . . .' Ian's voice faded altogether and Simoni sat down again on the chair, her whole body trembling because of the shame and humiliation that engulfed her. She had not successfully hidden her feelings and Kent was now angry, speaking about her so disparagingly to Ian— A sudden hint of puzzlement momentarily took the place of Simoni's burning embarrassment. Ian was shortly to become her sister-in-law and it just didn't make sense for either him or Kent to be talking like that. . . . But they had spoken like that, and Simoni felt she hated Kent as the tears of mortification stung her eyes. 'He's horrid to talk about me like that after all we went through in the desert together. I never would have believed he could—' The tears rolled unchecked down her cheeks and it was a long, long while before she went into her room and got into bed. Kent could keep his job; she would leave immediately – tomorrow if there was a plane.

But of course Simoni could not leave so suddenly as that; she realized this the moment she was awoken the following morning by the sun streaming through the window. Cindy would want a reason for the sudden decision to leave. Besides, Simoni still worked for Kent, Ian not yet having taken the children away from him.

At breakfast she scarcely looked at Kent, and when

he spoke to her she answered in monosyllables. Repeatedly he glanced at her with an uncomprehending expression and so did the others, and Cindy even went as far as to say, a hint of humour in her voice,

'What's up, Simoni? Got out the wrong side of the bed?' Kent looked oddly at her then, clearly interested in Simoni's response. She merely said, her voice cool and unemotional,

'I'm not feeling too good this morning,' which was very true, although intentionally misleading.

Simoni happened to be in the sitting-room when Kent was leaving for the office. He was alone this morning, Ian having gone in his own car a few minutes earlier. To Simoni's dismay Kent stopped and entered. He carried his briefcase, and also other papers in a folder under his arm.

'Are you feeling any better?' He sounded concerned, she thought, and wondered why. Any anxiety over her health could only stem from the fact of her having charge of the children, but as Cindy had now virtually taken over Simoni did not see why Kent should care whether she was feeling better or not.

'I'm just about the same.' Deliberately she turned her back on him and looked through the east-facing window. It was early, but the sun was already warm, shedding yellow light on to the sea and highlighting the jagged peaks of the Kyrenia massif, naked peaks carved and moulded through thousands of years of erosion when unvegetated soil was washed away by the heavy rains. Just below these summits the mountains were clothed with pine trees while lower still the slopes sweeping to the sea were dominated by the carob trees and olives, with here and there a date palm outlined against the sky.

A faintly bitter smile curved Simoni's mouth. Her thoughts were far removed from the lovely peaceful scene of sun and green hills and a blue unmoving sea.

'What is it?' Kent's voice, a little sharp now, she thought. 'There's something strange about you this morning, Simoni.'

'It's nothing. I'll be all right in a little while.' A little while? Simoni had the unhappy conviction that it would be a very long while before she was all right.

'You're quite sure?'

She nodded, forcing a smile, and to her relief he seemed reassured and a moment later she was watching his tall figure as he strode gracefully towards the place where his car was parked. 'I must leave,' quivered Simoni. 'I must!'

Cindy stared disbelievingly when Simoni expressed her intention of going home.

'But I don't understand.' Cindy stared at her, searching her face. 'This morning at breakfast there was something wrong with you. What is it, Simoni?' And then, her eyes opening wide with a mixture of comprehension and disbelief, 'The children – you think I shouldn't – I mean, they're really in your charge—' Cindy broke off because Simoni was shaking her head.

'You know me better than that, Cindy. Of course it isn't the children.'

'You don't resent my – well, I suppose it's inter-ference, really?'

'Certainly not. And I wouldn't call it interference. No, Cindy, I just want to go home, so please do me a favour and don't ask any more questions.' A sharp note entered her voice; it was unintentional and her eyes shaded apologetically. 'Sorry to be so moody, but I'm afraid I'm not feeling quite myself this morning.'

'Can I take the children to school for you?'

'Will you? Thanks, Cindy.'

'You're not ill, are you?' Cindy was anxious and Simoni shook her head, managing a smile, and Cindy added, 'Do you want anything from town while I'm there?'

'You can collect a book I've ordered from Yannis. You know his shop – opposite the Dome?'

'Yes, I know it.'

Simoni remained composed until the car had gone and then, unable to hold back her tears a moment longer, she put her face in her hands and wept. After a little while, afraid Cindy would return, Simoni went upstairs to her room. She did not hear Kent's car crunch along the lane, nor did the sound of the engine penetrate when the car came more smoothly along the drive. In fact, Simoni had no idea Kent was in the house until she heard his voice as he knocked on her door.

'Simoni, I'm coming in.' And without waiting for permission to enter he pushed open the door. Completely put out of countenance, Simoni turned abruptly away, frantically dabbing a handkerchief to her eyes.

'What do you want – I mean, why have you turned back?' Her voice caught now and then, because of the ache of tears in her throat.

He had stopped at the village shop, Kent explained, and had as usual put his car round the side because of the narrowness of the road. While in the shop he had seen Cindy pass with the children.

'What's wrong this morning? I demand to know!'

She turned then, acknowledging to herself the impossibility of avoiding embarrassment.

'I heard you and Ian talking about me last night.' Her face was pale, her voice edged with reproach. 'You should be ashamed of yourself for discussing me like that with my future brother-in-law.'

Staring at her uncomprehendingly, Kent advanced slowly into the room.

'You overheard Ian and me discussing you?' He frowned and shook his head, to all outward appearances completely at a loss. 'You'd better explain.'

'You know very well what you said,' she flashed, disgusted at this pretence and yet at the same time quivering with shame and anger and wishing she could run from him before she broke down and indulged in that form of self-pity he had once said he could not stand. 'I've no intention of repeating it, if that's what you're waiting for!'

A sharp intake of his breath betrayed his impatience.

'That's exactly what I am waiting for!' His tones were curt and imperious, the tones of Captain Kent Travers, her superior, and Simoni should have been warned by them. But for the moment the emotions of anger and humiliation enveloped her, occupying all her mind.

'Then you'll wait for ever!'

'I think not, Simoni.' Softly dangerous his tones now – and still she failed to take warning.

'You actually expect me to suffer further embarrassment by repeating what I heard?' She subjected him to a contemptuous glance, a glance he had never before received in his life. 'You're detestable!' She turned her back on him, but it was only for a second; she was jerked back to face him again, her cry of protest resulting only in a tightening of the painful grip on her arms.

'What did you hear?' he demanded wrathfully, but she would not tell him.

'My arms – you're hurting me—' Her words trailed off to an incoherent stammer as Kent shook her roughly.

'Answer me!' he thundered. 'Answer me – and stop talking in these damned riddles!'

She caught her lower lip between her teeth, endeavouring to stem her tears.

'I don't know why you should insist that I repeat—'

'Because I don't know what the devil you're talking about!' he blazed. 'What's the matter with you that you're so obtuse? Isn't it plain that I haven't the faintest idea what this is all about?'

Her eyes opened wide, searching his face. It was clear from his expression that he spoke the truth, for mingling with the fury was a baffled look which, she supposed, had been there all the time, but she had been so angry herself that she had failed to notice it.

'You weren't talking about me?' she queried in a small voice, and to her surprise his teeth gritted.

'If you don't tell me what I'm supposed to have said I shan't be responsible for my actions!' His grip tightened almost viciously. She could not tell whether or not it was an intentional act, but he did release her on seeing the tears start to her eyes.

'You were expressing annoyance because I was – I mean, because someone was in – in love with you. . . .' Who could it be? she wondered, swallowing convulsively on noting his expression. Scared of him she had been on many occasions, but now she realized she was actually afraid. 'I th-thought you were talking about me,' she added feebly, unaware of what she had revealed until she noticed the strange kindling of his eyes. She blushed then, and lowered her head. How stupid she had been! Had she not jumped to the wrong conclusions last night she would not now have given herself away. What must he think of her? Simoni could not bear to dwell on the humiliating fact that she had just made a confession of love and she said, in a cracked little voice that was intended to be light, 'It was silly of me – I see that now. But there's no harm done.' She laughed, lifting her head, but soon found her arms gripped again as Kent said, in a very soft tone,

'I ought to shake you good and hard. Why do women eavesdrop and, having done so, twist what they've heard so that it becomes totally different from what it really was? God, Simoni, there have been times in the past when I'd have liked to shake you till your teeth rattled, but never have I been so provoked as I am now!'

She stood very still, afraid he would carry out his threat, even while wondering at his short memory. For he had already shaken her unmercifully, to say nothing of the bruises he had left on her arms.

'I'm very sorry,' she murmured lamely at last, and then, 'I shouldn't have listened.'

'You should not!'

She glanced up at him, puzzled now by this little scene, with Kent so close, holding her arms in a proprietorial sort of way which seemed in itself to create an intimacy between them, for this was not the sort of drama one would expect to be enacted between two people who were merely friends.

The silence, broken only by the piercing notes of the cicadas in the trees outside, suddenly became oppressive and Simoni searched her mind for something to say.

'And – and as long as I did listen,' she uttered at last with a sort of floundering haste, 'I should have been more cautious and not drawn the wrong conclusions.' She was still extremely puzzled by the conversation she had overheard, out there in the garden.

'Had you practised this caution,' said Kent in biting tones, 'you'd obviously have saved yourself a good deal of misery.' She said nothing and he added, 'If you're interested in knowing who was under discussion, it was Thora Benson.'

'Thora? Is she leaving? I mean, it was because Ian said I – she—' Simoni broke off and started again. 'This person you were talking about was leaving in a fortnight and that's why I concluded it was me.'

'I've given Thora a fortnight's notice,' he explained, shaking his head in a little gesture of exasperation. 'Does that clear up all your ridiculous misconceptions?'

She nodded, yet looked uncertainly at him.

'The job, Kent? You said you were seeing about one for me.' Her breath was suddenly tight in her throat. The past few moments had sent her hopes soaring despite Kent's rather forbidding manner, but if he should now say he was intending to find her a job, then those hopes would instantly be dashed.

Ignoring her question, Kent asked one of his own.

'Seeing that you concluded it was you we were talking about, I suppose I'm right in thinking you love me?' Calm, unemotional words, but on glancing swiftly up at him Simoni thrilled to the gleam of tender amusement in his eyes.

'It wouldn't be much use my denying it,' she returned with a shaky little laugh.

'Not a bit.' His hands slid down her arms and she quivered under his touch. Gently she was drawn close to him and a trembling sigh was smothered as his lips found hers. She closed her eyes, surrendering herself up to this divine moment of fulfilment, and it was a long while before, holding her from him, he murmured tenderly, 'I've been an idiot, Simoni, fighting my love for you. I knew it was a losing battle and if I'd had any sense at all I'd have admitted it long ago.'

'You fought against your love?' She thought about that, remembering how she had suspected it. 'Why, Kent?' She was looking up into his face, all the bright radiance of adoration in her eyes.

He did not answer immediately, seeming to be absorbed by the darting activities of a charming little gecko on the wall.

'After my experience with Catherine I decided marriage was not for me. And as the years passed I must admit that my freedom became more and more attractive and I had no desire to lose it – no intention of losing it,' he added with a rueful laugh. 'But then you came along and, darling, I was finished!'

His words thrilled her and she snuggled close again and lifted her face for his kiss.

'When did you find out?' she wanted to know on recovering her breath a long while later. 'It wasn't at first, that was for sure!'

He laughed and shook his head.

'No, I wouldn't be honest if I said it was.' A pause and then, softly and inquiringly, 'Don't you know when it was?'

Through the open window came the tang of the sea, brought on a cooling breeze heralding the winter rains, those deluges that would soon be bringing life to the thirsty land. Carried on the breeze was the perfume of roses mingling with the sweet heady scent of lemon blossom flowering on the same trees as the shiny ripe fruit.

'Was it in the desert?' murmured Simoni at last, her voice dreamy and reflective.

'Yes, darling, it was in the desert.' Kent held her from him and his eyes kindled with amusement. 'I fell in love with a grubby-faced little girl with great dark shadows under her eyes and hair that looked like rats' tails.'

'You're horrid!'

He ignored that and asked,

'When did you discover your feelings? Was it also when we were in the desert?'

She shook her head, reluctant to mention that night at the Gulf Hotel. But as Kent was waiting she did eventually tell him that she was sure that incident was, for her, the beginnings of love.

'I'm sorry about that night, dearest,' Kent said with some regret. 'Forgive me?'

Her answer was a kiss, which she went on tiptoe to place upon his lips.

'It's a long time since we were in the desert,' she said, peeping at him through her lashes. 'You held out very well.'

'The defences were falling right from the start,' he owned, and she liked that. 'I'd never have got you the job, Simoni.'

'You said only yesterday that you would,' she reminded him, but he was shaking his head.

'I might have said it, but I didn't mean it. In fact, it was the thought of your getting a job and leaving the island that brought me to my senses at last. I wanted to have you alone last night, but you went to bed early – at least,' he added, obviously because he couldn't resist it, 'you were supposed to go to bed. So instead of my declaration of love you had a nasty few hours—'

'Few hours? It was an eternity!'

'Teach you not to eavesdrop!' he admonished swiftly. But he held her to him again and whispered, 'Darling, you'll marry me soon?'

She nodded, too full to speak, and with tender understanding Kent drew her head on to his shoulder and for a long while the only movement in the room was that of the dainty little lizard darting to and fro across the wall.

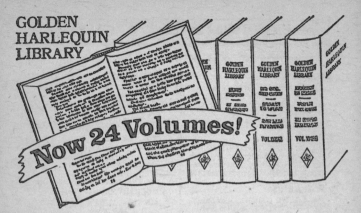

GOLDEN HARLEQUIN LIBRARY

Now 24 Volumes!

Harlequin readers will be delighted! We've collected seventy two of your all-time favourite Harlequin Romance novels to present to you in an attractive new way. It's the Golden Harlequin Library.

Each volume contains three complete, unabridged Harlequin Romance novels, most of which have not been available since the original printing. Each volume is exquisitely bound in a fine quality rich gold hardcover with royal blue imprint. And each volume is priced at an unbelievable $1.75. That's right! Handsome, hardcover library editions at the price of paperbacks!

This very special collection of 24 volumes (there'll be more!) of classic Harlequin Romances would be a distinctive addition to your library. And imagine what a delightful gift they'd make for any Harlequin reader!

Start your collection now. See reverse of this page for full details.

GOLDEN HARLEQUIN LIBRARY — $1.75 each volume